LOST VOYAGES OF TREK

AND THE

NEXT GENERATION

EDWARD GROSS

B⊞XTREE

First published in the UK 1995 by
BOXTREE Ltd
Broadwall House
21 Broadwall
London SE1 9PL

10 9 8 7 6 5 4 3 2 1

This publication is not licensed by, nor is Boxtree
affiliated with, Paramount Pictures. This is a scholarly work
intended to document the development of *Star Trek*

No photos appearing in this book are copyright
Paramount Pictures

Front cover photo copyright © G. Trindl/Shooting Star;
back cover photo copyright © David Strick/Onyx

ISBN 07522 0868 3

Typeset by SX Composing Ltd, Rayleigh, Essex
Printed and bound by Redwood Books, Trowbridge,
Wiltshire.

A catalogue record for this book is available from the
British Library

LOST VOYAGES:
AN INTRODUCTION

In researching the history of *Star Trek*, it becomes rather startling to see just how far this little science fiction show that couldn't (survive on network television) has come over the past 26 years.

Obviously it began with the 79 episodes making up the original series, now more commonly known as *Trek Classic*; but besides the phenomenal following the show garnered, it spawned 22 episodes of an animated spin-off, seven feature films, 178 episodes of the live action "sequel" *Star Trek: The Next Generation*, three seasons as of this date of the second spin-off, *Star Trek: Deep Space Nine*, the all-new *Star Trek: Voyager*, hundreds of books, at least 200 comic books, toys, lunchboxes and innumerable other items.

Star Trek endures. Whether you're a fan of the original show, *TNG, DS9* or *Voyager*, doesn't really matter. It has all become a part of the whole and, for the most part, the vast majority of fans look upon every aspect of Gene Roddenberry's creation as a single universe to admire and a vision for humanity to work toward achieving in reality.

Perhaps most surprising in the *Star Trek* mythos is the sheer quantity – and in many cases quality – of unfilmed adventures that have spanned from the original through various aborted attempts at revival throughout the 1970s and right in to *The Next Generation*. In many cases, these scripts and treatments were left unfilmed due to political reasons, studio indecisiveness or ego. In others, they just weren't up to snuff and probably wouldn't have made a decent episode of *Lost in Space*.

Lost Voyages of Trek and The Next Generation serves as a unique guidebook through the greatest *Trek* adventures that never were. You'll read of the unfilmed script co-written by genre great Norman Spinrad and series producer Gene L. Coon; the Enterprise's first penetration in to alien space as they voyage to the Klingon home world well before the events of the feature film *Star Trek VI: The Undiscovered Country*; the exploits of Enterprise officers Commander Will Decker, Lieutenant Ilia and Lieutenant Xon; Gene Roddenberry's last effort for *Star Trek*, a battle between crewmembers of *The Next Generation* and the living dead; and an unfilmed adventure featuring Q.

Join us on these voyages which no one has known before.

Edward Gross
November, 1994

TREK CLASSIC
"HE WALKED AMONG US"
Teleplay by Norman Spinrad and Gene L. Coon
Story by Norman Spinrad

As part of a routine periodic check on a developing culture, the Enterprise is in orbit around the planet Jugal, located within System NGC 489.

Spock announces that sensors detect electrical power, which the planet shouldn't have as they're supposedly at the first stages of urban development. He pipes through a sound from the planet: a steam whistle. Stating that someone has violated the Prime Directive, Kirk decides that they'll have to investigate. He, Spock, McCoy, Chekov and Uhura undertake a crash course in Jugal history and beam down in the appropriate clothing.

According to the script, the landing party – adorned in monk-like robes – have appeared outside the city wall. "Over the wall of the city appears the tower and roof of a typical Babylon-era small city ... adobe, simple, primitive ... perhaps one ziggurat-type tower in background. A few people pass in and out of the open gates, which are guarded by two soldiers of the Kar. They carry spears, wear swords. Like all the Jugalis, they are faintly green in color, with metallic-appearing hair."

The group moves through the gates and Spock, via tricorder, leads them toward the power source, but they are captured by a group of threatening Jugal warriors. They're hustled into the square, and approached by Lokar, the High Priest of Bayne. Kirk abruptly calls for phasers and his group starts firing.

At that moment, Kaneb, the soldier-king, appears. He's described as stocky, very muscular, the look of a warrior painted all over him. The soldiers, who have not actually seen the phasers, back away from the landing party. Kaneb is furious at his warriors' seeming weakness. When Kirk and company lower their hoods, everyone is stunned to see how different they look from natives of the planet.

"It is the prophecy of Bayne," proclaims Lokar. "These are his brothers, come from heaven. Let no Kar lay hands upon them, lest lightning strike them down. It is the word of Bayne."

Kaneb insists that these people come with him and it looks like there will be a major conflict between the two factions. As Spock points out, they appear to be in the middle of a power struggle between the secular and the clerical. Kirk agrees, and feels that the only solution is to go directly to Bayne, whoever he may be. To this end, the captain announces that Bayne has called them from beyond the stars and wishes to speak to them. Lokar proclaims the holiness of their words and leads them away.

In the so-called Great Hall of Bayne, they see the previously discussed steam engine. Bayne enters the room, and he's described as being "dressed in flowing robes, looking quite regal. Bayne is a largish, heavy man of great dignity ... .and just as obviously a Negro from earth." Bayne moves to his throne and mounts it, then welcomes the outsiders, acknowledging that he knew they would someday be coming. He explains that he had been Doctor Theodore Bayne, formerly of the Rigel Colonies, who is now quite comfortable in his position.

Kirk identifies himself as the captain of the Enterprise while Spock, who has been in contact with the ship, explains that he has obtained a personal dossier on the man. McCoy's heard of him, and "if he's the local tin god, these people are in for a lot of trouble." Chekov and Uhura are told to remain alert while Kirk, Spock and McCoy join Bayne in private. In the man's quarters, McCoy sarcastically comments that at last Bayne has a planet of his own to explore his "crackpot ideas." Kirk demands an explanation.

"He's one of those screwballs who thinks he can cure cancer with lots of cold water baths," replies McCoy. "A diet of fruit and nuts. He's been thrown off of every civilized planet he ever landed on."

Bayne dismisses this as the actions of stubborn and mistaken people who lacked true vision. It is then that Kirk realizes that the population does indeed look upon Bayne as a god. According to Bayne, it's deserved. In six years he has advanced the civilization a thousand years. Spock brings up the Prime Directive, which Bayne dismisses as bureaucratic red-tape. Nonetheless, Kirk wants him to go with them to the Enterprise.

Bayne doesn't believe this is a good idea, and points to the Prime Directive as a reason. He is the only thing holding this planet together. Without him, Jugal would explode into war between Lokar and Kaneb. Spock is forced to concur with this. Meanwhile, Chekov and Uhura are taken prisoner by Kaneb and his men, with Kaneb commenting, "Gods! More Gods! I am up to my knee plates in Gods. Well, then we will let the people see whether or not their Gods can die!"

Back in Bayne's quarters, the

"god" admits that he is not much of an engineer, and the steam engine is about all he could muster. Still, it provides lighting, pumps water to the nearby fields and is considered something of a holy object to the populace. Bayne believes he has done no harm whatsoever, while Kirk counters that his so-called gift has created economic havoc. Bayne is unmoved.

Spock approaches, emphasizing that Dr. McCoy's assessment of Bayne was correct; that the man had indeed been exiled from a variety of planets.

Bayne claims his ship had crashed on this planet and Kaneb found him. The planet, he emphasizes, was in chaos. Since then, things haven't gone that well between the two men, which Bayne chalks up to Kaneb's not understanding what he has been attempting to do. Kirk states that they *do* understand, and it can't be allowed to continue. All he has to do is make a public statement that he's been called back to heaven, arranging for peace before he departs. While admitting that such an action might be possible, Bayne refuses to participate.

Lokar bursts into the room, announcing that the soldiers of the Kar have taken Bayne's "brothers." Kirk deduces that the man is talking about Chekov and Uhura and withdraws his phaser. Bayne counters, stating that such a show of force will result in their deaths. Pulling out his communicator, Kirk contacts Scotty and has him lock on to Chekov and Uhura's coordinates. Bayne wonders why he doesn't save all of them a lot of trouble and have the duo transported up to the Enterprise.

"You'd like that, wouldn't you?" muses Kirk. "Have them disappear into thin air. Then there wouldn't be any doubt that we're all gods. Especially the Great Bayne."

Bayne smiles. "A little divinity comes in useful in this line of work, Captain."

Spock suggests that if they can prove that Bayne has done more harm than good, he would leave. Bayne, who feels his only purpose has been to help people, agrees. Kirk and Spock begin an investigation and quickly discern that Bayne has not only destroyed the economy, but ruined the plantations due to his limited knowledge of agriculture; and because he has insisted on monogamy, there are now too many women and not enough men. Prior to his arrival, each man had three wives and all were happy.

In Kaneb's palace, both Uhura and Chekov state that they have made no claims to be gods. This doesn't matter, Kaneb says, because the truth must be pointed out to the people — by killing the strangers in front of them. Kaneb proceeds to the castle's library where he encounters Bayne. Kaneb brings up the fact that his war is *not* with Lokar, but with Bayne himself. He will, however, let the people from the stars live if Bayne leaves with them. He refuses.

"I made a god of you, Theodore," says Kaneb. "You were a tool, like my sword! And a good one – for a while. But a sword can be dangerous – and so can a god. Theodore, I don't want to kill you, but I promise you that unless you leave with these humans, I will!"

"I am Bayne. These people are my people."

"A dead god serves only the roots of the grass he feeds."

Bayne finds this humorous, noting that people have a right to martyr their gods. Kaneb will not let Uhura and Chekov go.

As Kirk, Spock and McCoy compare notes on exactly what Bayne has done to this world, they realize they're going to have to rescue Chekov and Uhura themselves. They make their way to Kaneb's castle and move through the corridors of the dungeon. Within a cell they find their comrades. Kaneb and half a dozen archers appear around them. They, too, will be made an example of to the people on the following morning when they're executed.

Lokar, who's learned of events in the castle, goes to Bayne, informing him that his forces are preparing to invade the castle and rescue Bayne's brothers. Bayne forbids it, but Lokar can't afford to have the humans proved to be anything but gods in order to preserve his own base of power.

Bayne threatens to tell the people, but Lokar states that he'll only speak to the people when he (Lokar) commands it, and speak only the words that are given to him. In fact, from this day forward the men of Lokar will be just outside his door and wherever he goes. The rest of Lokar's plan unfolds as he explains that the "brother gods" will be killed, and that Bayne will command the taking of the Kar's life.

At this moment, Bayne realizes that he is a prisoner of his own godhead.

In the library, Spock, Kirk and Kaneb are in discussion about Bayne. Kaneb details how he made Bayne a god because the man knew the answer to all questions the war-torn people of Jugal had.

"And because he had all the answers," Kirk muses, "people stopped asking questions."

Kaneb concurs. No one thinks for themselves anymore. Kirk tries to explain that they are really there to help, because Bayne has broken one of their most important rules and for that must be taken away. Kaneb suggests that they take him immediately and everyone will live. Spock states that it is not quite as easy as that. If Bayne simply disappears, then Lokar would rule in his stead.

They just need a little more time to convince him. Kaneb's fear is that they, too, will set themselves up as gods. He cannot afford the risk and is about to give the order for them to be killed, but Kirk dives across the table and wraps his chains around the man's neck, demanding the keys to unlock them. Kirk tightens his grip on Kaneb until the guards give them back their phasers and communicators. They use the weapons to stun Kaneb and his men. Kirk wants them to head back to Bayne's castle, because that's the place where Kaneb's troops won't follow. Regarding Bayne himself, Spock believes that they have incontrovertible evidence that the man is causing great harm, so he will leave.

In a sly in-joke, McCoy replies, "You know it's incontrovertible, and so do I, but you're not going to convince that screwball. I know I'm supposed to be the humanitarian, but there's only one way to do this. Use a club on him."

Only if they have to, Kirk responds. They proceed to their destination, Kirk telling Scotty to have a voice-amplifier standing by. They enter the Great Hall of Bayne, and tell Lokar that Kaneb's men may try to get in. Lokar states that the word of Bayne will prevail and leads them to Bayne's quarters.

Bayne is immediately apologetic, having never realized that things could get so far out of hand. This, Kirk says, is the reason that the Prime Directive exists. At last, Bayne is convinced that he must tell his people that he has been called back to heaven and that Kaneb will rule in his place.

"Will you open your eyes, Mr. Bayne?" Kirk demands. "Lokar won't let you make a statement like that. There are only two ways you'll be any good to him: alive and under his control – or martyred by Kaneb!"

Kirk decides that the proper course of action will be to make a god – a real god – out of Bayne. Spock finds it difficult to understand exactly how he will do this. At that moment, Lokar approaches and tells them that a living god is much more trouble than it's worth. Bayne will die along with them, and the people, furious that their god has been murdered, will turn their hatred

toward the Kar. Bayne shall live on through the word of Lokar and he shall rule.

After Lokar departs, Spock admits that there does not seem to be any logical solution to the problem. No matter what happens, the people of Jugal will suffer greatly. Kirk reminds him that he is forgetting genuine, registered, officially certified godhood.

Kirk's plan, only partially revealed at this point, is for he and Uhura to beam aboard the ship, which leaves the rest of them damn close to the executioner's block. To this end, Kirk refers to a situation on Eminiar 7 ["A Taste of Armageddon"] where Spock willed a guard into believing they were attempting escape, thus luring him into their cell. He suggests that Spock try it again. The trick works and they gain the upper hand, Kirk dispatches a guard with a series of judo chops and Spock utilizes the FSNP (the Famous Spock Nerve Pinch). It's Kirk opinion that Lokar is going to treat Bayne with a little more respect from this point on.

The group moves into the Great Hall and find that the steam engine is unwatched. They appear from a door behind the throne – the one that Bayne usually makes his entrances from – and seal it with a bar. Kirk points out positions for Spock and Chekov to take in the hall, to protect them. He sends Bayne to his throne and McCoy out in a protective position. Kirk and Uhura notice that the level of steam is down and they start throwing stacks of firewood into the proper chamber. The fire burns brighter as they hear shouts from outside, the unconscious guards presumably having been found. Kirk instructs Uhura to send Scotty their coordinates with a pick up order. Due to the fact that the minute they hear the whistle everyone will be on them, Uhura has to hurry.

According to the script, on Kirk's signal "Uhura grabs the hanging rope,

starts to pull in a short, choppy, very quick sequence. The noise is deafening. It should *not* be Morse Code. This is sub-space code, something entirely different, in which long messages can be sent very quickly . . . a form of short hand. But all brace themselves, knowing that the great noise will shortly attract Lokar's men."

Lokar orders them to be killed as he and his warriors burst into the room. A fight between "them and us" immediately ensues. Bayne sits on his throne, horrified by the violence unfolding before him. McCoy and Chekov are knocked down, and Spock is starting to lose ground to the overwhelming numbers. In a moment seemingly inspired by *The Wizard of Oz*, Lokar catches sight of Kirk behind the steam engine and shouts, "Behind the voice of Bayne!"

At that moment, Kirk and Uhura are transported up. Lokar is awed by their disappearance, but fights for control. He approaches Chekov, McCoy and Spock, demanding to know where Kirk and Uhura went. "I am sure you will find this difficult to believe, sir," Spock replies dryly, "but they were lifted bodily to the stars." Lokar is shaken.

In the Enterprise transporter room, Scotty wants to send down a security team to "clean out the whole nest of them," but Kirk responds that they can't interfere anymore than they already have. As it is, things are going to be difficult to explain to Starfleet Command.

Bayne's Quarters: Lokar is still demanding to know where the others are. Spock repeats his statement from earlier. Bayne reiterates his godhood, but Lokar is dismissive of him, stating that the Kar will kill him and Lokar will rule all of Jugal. At that moment, Kaneb and his men break into the room.

The steam whistle blows again, with Kirk, dressed in his hooded robe, materializing. In his hand is a voice amplifier. A procession moves toward the throne, with Kirk whispering into his communicator, giving the coordinates of Spock, McCoy and Chekov. He instructs Scotty to energize first at the throne and then on those coordinates at his command.

Lokar calls for them to listen to the words of Bayne so that they will be enlightened. Kaneb refuses, claiming that no god can bleed and he will prove it on Bayne. As Kaneb moves forward, Kirk speaks into the voice amplifier, "Stop, O Kar!" As the writers detail, "The voice booms, from every corner of the great hall. It comes from nowhere, everywhere . . . and it sounds like the crack of doomsday, like Peter's trumpet." Everyone is stunned, including Kaneb. Kirk continues, claiming that it is the time for the return of the gods to heaven, and that the people of Jugal are not worthy of their continued presence. It is their stubbornness and willfulness that has cost them their gods. Even Kaneb protests, but Kirk notes that "it is done." An instant later, Bayne is transported away. The people in the room are consumed with fear and awe. Then Spock, Chekov and McCoy vanish.

Kirk addresses the crowd, voice booming, and demanding peace. Kar, he says, will rule from the throne while Lokar will rule from the altar.

Lokar proclaims Bayne's divinity and then bows to Kaneb, stating that he will rule with the blessings of Bayne. Kaneb returns the bow, stating that no one should say that Bayne was not a god, adding that there will be peace between Kar and Priest on Jugal, between man and god. Greatly relieved, Kirk has himself beamed up.

After the Enterprise leaves orbit, we cut to the bridge. Kirk is pleased with himself, pointing out that before long the people of Jugal will forget

exactly what it was that Bayne stood for and will revert to their natural ways. Spock agrees, adding that perhaps in 100 years or so it will seem as though Bayne had never been there at all, except as a legend. At that moment, Bayne enters the bridge from the turbo lift, agitated because steak is being served for dinner. Additionally, the water is fluoridated, the fruits and vegetables grown with chemical fertilizers, the electronic cook peels the potatoes, etc. At least now that he's on board, he'll be able to do something about these "frightful evils." Kirk cuts him off, telling McCoy to take Bayne to sickbay and give him a dose of liver extract. Bayne is incredulous, as is Bones, but the two men depart the bridge.

"A somewhat peremptory manner in which to treat a god, Captain," says Spock.

"By the time we're through with Mr. Bayne, he'll be a mortal again. Of course, I'm not so sure about you, Mr. Spock. I've got a feeling you enjoyed your brief moment of divinity."

"It had its pleasant aspects, Captain. But I was unable to enjoy it completely." Off Kirk's quizzical stare he continues, "My divinity was shared by five humans. It quite took away the charm."

* * *

The concept of a member of Starfleet breaking the Prime Directive and corrupting an alien society with Captain Kirk as the chosen officer to set things right, was certainly nothing new in the Star Trek mythos. None, however, had really dealt with the concept of one of our people using the advanced technology to set himself up as a god to the populace. This would have been done to great effect in "He

Walked Among Us," and to see how easily Enterprise or other starship personnel could be perceived as gods, one should check out the "Who Watches the Watchers?" episode of Star Trek: The Next Generation.

Writer Norman Spinrad, who had penned the original Trek first season episode "The Doomsday Machine," co-wrote the teleplay for "He Walked Among Us" with the late Gene L. Coon. According to Spinrad, it was not one of his favorite collaborations.

"They wanted me to write another episode," he explains, "and they gave me two things. They sent me to a backlot way out in Culver City, which was overgrown with weeds, where they had this weird village set. Then, they told me that Milton Berle wanted to do a Star Trek. So, I had Milton Berle and this village. I know that Berle can be a serious actor, but he likes weird get-ups. I said, 'OK, let Milton Berle be a messiah,' and that was the germ of the idea. Milton Berle would go to an alien planet and be set up as a god.

"Gene Coon, in his wisdom as my story editor, said, 'This script needs a rewrite. Who can I trust to rewrite it? Well, I know somebody who has never disappointed me.' He did it himself. Basically he rewrote a serious anthropological piece of material into something being played for laughs. I was so pissed off that I called up Roddenberry and said, 'Gene, you cannot do this. You have to kill this script,' and he agreed to do that. I killed my own script rather than have it presented in that way."

One can only assume that the more humorous version was a later draft than the one summarized above, for it's difficult to imagine Milton Berle in any of the key roles.

THE RETURN OF STAR TREK 1975–77

THE GOD THING (1975)

The first attempt at reviving *Star Trek* came with Gene Roddenberry's 1975 script for *The God Thing*.

"They turned me down a couple of times," said Roddenberry regarding a film version of the series, "then they finally said, 'Write a script and we'll give you an office on the lot and think about it.' They were not that serious about [it] when we first started. I think they had in mind a $2-$3 million picture."

Added William Shatner, "I was working on the series *Barbary Coast*, which was done at Paramount. It was on one end of Paramount and *Star Trek* had been filmed on the other end of Paramount. I had not, for the longest time, revisited the stage area where [we had] filmed. So one day I decided to go there, [and] as I'd been walking and remembering the times, I suddenly heard the sound of a typewriter! That was the strangest thing, 'cause these offices were deserted. So I followed the sound, till I came to the entrance of this building. I went down a hallway, where the offices for *Star Trek* were … I opened the door and there was Gene Roddenberry! He was sitting in a corner typing. I hadn't seen him in five years. I said, 'Gene, the series has been canceled.' He said, 'I know, I know the series has been cancelled. I'm writing the movie!' So I said, 'There's gonna be a movie? What's it gonna be about?' He said, 'First of all, we have to explain how you guys got older. So what we have to do is move everybody up a rank. You become an Admiral, and the rest of the cast become Starfleet Com-manders. One day a force comes toward Earth – might be God, might be the Devil – breaking everything in its path, except the minds of the starship commanders. So we gotta find all the original crewmen for the starship Enterprise, but first – where is Spock? He's back on Vulcan, doing R&R; five year mission – seven years of R&R. He swam back upstream. So we gotta go get him.' I call that show, 'What Makes Salmon Run?' So we get Spock, do battle and it was a great story, but the studio turned it down."

Although little is known about the resulting script, reports have stated that the premise questioned the very nature of God and the universe around us. Paramount was apparently not interested in a script which, essentially, pit Captain Kirk against God.

Director Richard Colla, who had helmed Roddenberry's *The Questor Tapes*, was very familiar with that particular screenplay and recalls it fondly.

"That script was much more daring," he reflects. "They went off in search of that thing from outer space that was affecting everything. By the time they got on to the spaceship and got into its [the alien's] presence, it manifested itself and said, 'Do you know me?' Kirk said, 'No, I don't know who you are.' It said, 'Strange, how could you not know who I am?' So it shift-changed and became another image and said, 'Do you know me?' Kirk said, 'No, who are you?' It replied, 'The time has passed and you should know me by now.' It shifts shapes again and comes up in the form of Christ the Carpenter, and says, 'Do you know me?' and Kirk said, 'Oh, now I know who you are.' And he says, 'How strange you didn't know these other forms of me.' Really, what Gene had written was that this 'thing' was sent forth to lay down the law; to communicate the law of the universe, and that as time goes on the law needs to be reinterpreted. And at that time 2,000 years ago, the law was interpreted by this Carpenter image. As time went on, the law was meant to be reinterpreted, and the Christ figure was meant to reappear in different forms. But this machine malfunctioned, and it was like a phonograph record that got caught in a groove and kept grooving back, grooving back, grooving back. It's important to understand the essence of all this and reinterpret it as time goes on. That was a little heavy for Paramount. It was meant to be strong and moving, and I'm sorry it never got made."

Of the climactic moment when the alien takes on the form of Christ, William Shatner wrote in the pages of *Star Trek Movie Memories*, "'You *must* help me!' the probe repeats, now bleeding from hands, feet and forehead. Kirk refuses, at which point the probe begins exhausting the last of its energy in a last-ditch violent rampage, commanding the Enterprise crew to provide the assistance it needs to survive. Without warning, the force summons up the last of its remaining strength to blast Sulu, severing the crewman's legs in the process. When Spock attempts to comfort the mortally wounded Sulu, he, too, is blasted and left for dead. With that expenditure of energy, the vessel is weakened to the point of vulnerability, and the Enterprise unleashes a barrage of firepower that destroys the craft.

"'With that,' says Gene, 'we begin pondering the notion that perhaps mankind has finally evolved to the point where it's outgrown its need for gods, competent to account for its own behavior without the religiously imposed concepts of fear, guilt or divine intervention.'"

While incredibly impressed and intrigued by Roddenberry's script, Shatner nonetheless felt that no studio in its right corporate mind would greenlight *The God Thing*. He was right.

"I handed them a script and they turned it down," Roddenberry stated. "It was too controversial. It talked about concepts like, 'Who is God?' [In it] the Enterprise meets God in space; God is a life form, and I wanted to suggest that there may have been, at one time in the human beginning, an alien entity that early man believed was God, and kept those legends. But I also wanted to suggest that it might have been as much the Devil as it was God. After all, what kind of god would throw humans out of Paradise for eating the fruit of the Tree of Knowledge? One of the Vulcans on board, in a very logical way, says, 'If this is your God, he's not very impressive. He's got so many psychological problems; he's so insecure. He demands worship every seven days. He goes out and creates faulty humans and then blames them for his own mistakes. He's a pretty poor excuse for a supreme being.' Not surprisingly, that didn't send the Paramount executives off crying with glee. But I think good science fiction, historically, has been used that way – to question *everything*."

Back in the '70s, Roddenberry claimed that he was adapting this screenplay into novel form. Although it was supposed to have been published posthumously in the fall of 1992 as a special hardcover edition from Pocket Books, it never appeared.

STAR TREK II (1975)

The film opens with three starship captains in different situations, giving the order to fire on some one or some thing and the subsequent destruction of the unidentified targets.

The scene shifts to a Federation hearing room where a Vulcan diplomat is claiming that the Starfleet vessels acted aggressively in situations in which the provocation was questionable. The Vulcan representative then *demands* that Earth be relieved of its duties as the planet in charge of Starfleet operations. Earth refuses. Starfleet regulations, however, are that the commanding planet must relinquish command in response to any legitimate request from any other Federation Member. Arguing that Vulcan's request is *not* legitimate, Earth asks for, and is granted, a hearing before the Federation Council.

At the hearing (attended by Admiral Kirk), Earth justifies the three incidents reasonably well and points out that Vulcan did not *request* that Earth relinquish command, it (Vulcan) *demanded* it. The Earth representatives point out that this is very hot-blooded behavior for the usually cool Vulcans and that something seems very strange about their position and general attitude. The Vulcan representatives indicate that they simply feel that Earth is becoming a bit lax in observance of the Prime Directive and that it is time to find another planet to administrate Starfleet that will be somewhat more hesitant to use force. They apologize for the use of the word demand, agreeing that it was a poor choice, but that, logically, a request is the same as a demand because Federation laws dictate that Earth *must* relinquish command any time another Federation planet formally expresses legitimate dissatisfaction with the

way the command planet is exercising its command. When both sides have finished presenting their cases, the Council deliberates and finds in favor of Earth. The Vulcan representatives claim that they have been left no logical alternative but to withdraw from the Federation, and that is what they do.

The Council is stunned. After the Vulcan representatives leave, there is general agreement that something must be amiss for these events to be occurring. As the only commanding officer ever to bring back a relatively whole starship and crew after a five year mission, Kirk is instructed to take the Enterprise and go to Vulcan to see if he can discover what the real problem is and work it out. For the time being, Vulcan shall be considered a semi-hostile planet by all members of the Federation.

Kirk reassembles as much of his old crew as possible for the mission, understandably crediting them with much of the success of the five year mission. Spock is missing, and presumably somewhere on Vulcan.

The ship arrives at Vulcan to find the planet swathed in an impenetrable force field. When Kirk asks for permission to beam down, he is refused and told to leave the Vulcan Solar System. The Enterprise will be considered a hostile presence if it is not gone within two hours. They leave the system but just barely, leaving the elliptic and traveling just beyond the distance of the farthest planet a few minutes journey at warp two. Once there, Kirk considers and finally determines that since this problem has to do primarily with Vulcan, Spock's assistance seems absolutely essential. Sensor readings are completely normal, nothing seems out of the ordinary except the Vulcan behavior. To do anything at all about it, he must first understand it and to understand it, he must somehow get down to the planet's surface and talk to some trusted friends, some of whom should be able to tell him where Spock is.

Kirk has McCoy perform plastic surgery on him to make him look Vulcan. At the same time, he has Scotty prepare a small anti-force ring, which, for a short time, can soak up all the energy of a small area of the force field. The Enterprise will re-enter the solar system at warp six and stop on a dime. Then the ring will be placed on the outer edge of the field by a shuttle craft and Kirk will be quickly beamed through it to the planet's surface. The Enterprise will then leave the area at warp six as soon as the shuttlecraft returns. They will return to the planet for two minutes at a time, for communications purposes, according to a staggered synchronized schedule that Kirk leaves with Scotty. The ship will always come and go at warp six, a speed on the wrong side of the safety margins, the idea being to come and go unnoticed as much as possible, and not to hang around long enough to seem a threat when they *are* noticed.

The operation is performed. The maneuver is executed. Kirk is beamed down perfectly into the house of a friend. He is greeted frostily – with considerable mistrust. The friend will tell Kirk nothing. The only thing he will do, for the sake of their former friendship, is that he will not report Kirk's presence if he leaves at once. It again seems that very un-Vulcan things are happening – both the mistrust and the contradictory act of sentiment for an old friendship. Kirk does leave at once.

Remaining anonymous in city crowds, Kirk gradually begins to get some insight into what is happening. There is a universal mistrust in the air. Mistrust of the entire Federation. Mistrust of everyone except, perhaps, the Romulans, because they are of the same stock. Also, the Vulcans are eating meat again, and talking angry interstellar politics in groups of concerned citizens. Kirk overhears that Spock and his mother have been arrested as someone argues that Sarek should be confined as well. Kirk, as just another concerned Vulcan, asks if the confinement is safe enough, and in the resulting conversation is able to find out where Spock is and what security he will have to go through. Timing his entry to a communications time with the Enterprise, he breaks into the detainment center and finds Spock.

Spock, who has been meditating, immediately tells Kirk that he will not be a party to any hostile activities against Vulcan. Kirk tells him to argue later and yanks out his communicator. Spock and Kirk fight for it – but it falls down, open, and that is enough for Scotty, who beams them aboard in the middle of the fight. Spock cannot return because the ring only lasts for a few seconds and the shuttlecraft would have to place another one down in order to transport back again.

Spock is confined behind a forcefield on board. Kirk attempts to convince him that the Federation is *not* plotting against Vulcan and that his (Spock's) assistance will not be used against the planet. Asked what could make him believe that humans were anti-Vulcan, Spock points out the constant ribbing, insults and insinuations that he lived with for five years on board the Enterprise. That without even thinking about it, humans smugly assume that their way is the proper way and that all other ways must be "good naturedly tolerated" – not respected; not considered valuable and valid, just tolerated. It is quite easy to understand that even a Vulcan could grow hostile from this. But it's impossible for Kirk to understand, although he agrees that humans have treated Vulcans in the way described – but that Vulcans have always understood and tolerated such treatment. Something strange, he muses, must have happened for that understanding to have degenerated so quickly, for Vulcans to have suddenly acquired a full set of negative emotions. Spock reminds Kirk that Vulcans have always had

emotions, they simply chose to exercise their wills to suppress them.

Kirk tells Spock that he'd better decide what he wants to do. The Vulcans confined him because he is half-human and they felt they could no longer trust him. Kirk adds that he feels he knows Spock better than any man in the universe and that Spock knows him equally well. Somewhere inside, Spock must realize that he can trust Kirk. Recognizing this, Kirk tells Spock to find that trust and act on it because if they don't stop whatever is happening, it will degenerate into a war. Spock replies that he is a Vulcan. Kirk screams, "You sonofabitch, you're human, too! Think about it." and he storms out. Spock silently prepares to meditate but as he does so, a tear rolls down his cheek. He struggles with himself until he can take it no more. He breaks down and cries with his entire being, then slips into meditation.

Kirk calls a meeting to get everyone else's thoughts on the next move. One proposal is that since the only time Vulcans were like this was in the past, perhaps the place to look is in the past. It seems about the best anyone can come up with and Kirk decides to try a dangerous time warp. He tells Scotty to prepare engineering while he will continue to try to find a way to reach Spock.

Resting in his quarters, Kirk is surprised to discover that Spock has managed to turn off the forcefield and escape. At that moment, he realizes that the Vulcan seems positively jovial, to which Spock responds that through sheer will power he has been able to release his human half. Only by staying human will be able to fight off the effect of the source of Vulcan's current problem. He is, therefore, controlling himself to be as human as possible, and he hopes that Kirk and the rest of the crew will be able to put up with him. It won't be easy, because this Spock lacks the discipline of a soldier.

It's Spock's opinion that a

psychic cloud released from Vulcan centuries ago is responsible. It had been designed as a weapon that would making opposing forces mistrust their commanders and cause fighting amongst themselves. Apparently it was unleashed against an enemy during Vulcan's final war. Exactly how has remained a mystery, but it didn't work the way it had been designed – thought emanations were only receivable by Vulcans. The enemy was destroyed in a major battle shortly thereafter and the cloud was thought to have dissipated. Apparently not, because the planet's inhabitants have certainly undergone a change, which the human part of Spock recognizes.

The best thing to do, according to Spock, is to time warp back and try to prevent the release of the cloud. Kirk concurs. The ship is readied and the maneuver executed. Spock and Kirk beam down to ancient Vulcan to begin their search for the psychic generator – a very small needle in a very large haystack.

It is not hard to see why Vulcans had to learn to control and repress all emotion in order to survive. These Vulcans are indeed hot-blooded people: lusty and energetic, quick to anger and fiercely proud. The only resemblance to modern Vulcans is that they seem to display no fear in battle. In a fighting situation, they remain cool, level-headed, highly efficient instruments of destruction. It is as though the anger builds up until it triggers the cool destructive fighter to come out. Nevertheless, the war is not going well at all. They are fighting an enemy that is more advanced than they are, and their backs are against the wall. Their space has been largely decimated and they expect a fresh attack at any moment. The Enterprise, in fact, might well be interpreted as an advance wave of some sort and draw a response from the planet. This is indeed what happens, but the Enterprise is fairly secure behind its screens, and when it makes no move to attack, the Vulcans eventually discontinue wasting firepower on it.

Meanwhile, Starfleet gets impatient and breaks communications silence to call the Enterprise in order to get a progress report. When they get no response, they assume that the ship has been destroyed. Before declaring an open war, other ships will be sent in to investigate. The two closest starships are instructed to proceed immediately to planet Vulcan.

Spock and Kirk begin to make some progress in their search for the generator. It turns out that it is being considered the last hope for the planet. The project is being rushed to completion in a secret compound near the southern pole by a single scientist who was laughed at for many years, but who is now being looked upon as a savior. The generator is totally his creation and he won't let anyone else near it. The only way Spock and Kirk will be able to get there is to get the exact location of the compound and then have the Enterprise beam them there.

As they discover the location, a fresh attack is launched against the planet. When they are transported to the compound, the scientist instantly assumes them to be the enemy. The moment he sees Spock and Kirk materializing, he hits a series of buttons, finishing just as their bodies become complete. He tells them that they are too late, that the seeds of their army's destruction have been sown even as they arrived and that there is no way to bring them back. Spock, who has been acting charmingly erratic ever since releasing his human half, whips out his phaser and kills the scientist. Kirk is stunned. In addition to the moral issue, he points out that they might have been able to convince the scientist that their intentions were friendly and elicit his aid. Spock claims he saw the scientist's hand reaching for a button which Spock assumed would be a destruct button. He had to shoot before the hand

reached the button because the weapon holds their only chance to prevent the impending war. Spock would have preferred to shoot to stun, but there wasn't time to change the setting. They check the panel and there is, indeed, a destruct button there. Whether or not that was the button the scientist was going for (if he was even reaching for a button at all) is strictly a matter of conjecture. This sequence of events seems to corroborate history. The mysterious circumstance said to surround the release of the cloud was the intervention of Spock and Kirk.

As the duo prepare the machinery to be beamed up to the ship, Spock finds a small device which can fit in the palm of his hand and pockets it. The two men then transport up with the psychic generator. As soon as they are back on board, Spock asks the status of the space battle between Vulcan and its opponent. He is told that in the last few moments things seem to have taken a turn for the worse for the Vulcans. They had been holding their own until a few minutes earlier when they inexplicably broke formation. They now seem to be in considerable trouble. Spock expected this. He tells Kirk it is imperative that the Enterprise enter the battle on behalf of the Vulcans. Kirk is hesitant. He knows from history that Vulcan won the battle, and he wants Spock to work on reversing the psychic generator. Spock removes the device he pocketed. It is a hypnotic inducer. Spock hypnotizes Kirk and suggests that they both go up to the bridge to study the matter further before deciding what action to take. Kirk (in a barely noticeable trance) affably agrees.

When they arrive on the bridge, the situation has already worsened. It is clear that none of the Vulcan ships are cooperating as a result of the psychic cloud. Spock suggests to Kirk that the Enterprise go to battle status and that he be given command status because he is more familiar with how

the battle was fought historically. Kirk calmly agrees. Spock leads the ship through a series of rapid maneuvers, turning and firing in quick succession. In a very short time, the enemy is completely destroyed. Spock secures from battle stations and takes Kirk back to the psychic generator. He programs what Kirk will remember and what he won't with hypnotic suggestion and then releases him from the trance.

Kirk asks how long it will be before Spock will be able to do anything with the machine. Spock isn't sure, but asks to be left alone with it. Spock examines the machine for a short time, completes a few connections, presses a few buttons, raises an eyebrow and sits in front of the machine to meditate.

While Spock meditates, the situation around present day Vulcan is becoming very explosive. The two starships that Starfleet sent to Vulcan are now in orbit, joined by perhaps one or two others. Opposite them is a small fleet of Vulcan vessels. Starfleet wants to know what happened to the Enterprise. The Vulcans want the Federation ships out of their space. Both sides sit at red alert. Finally, the Vulcans issue an ultimatum. The starships must leave within five minutes or a state of war will exist. The vessels don't budge.

On board the Enterprise, McCoy barges in on Spock and is absolutely infuriated that Spock is just sitting there, not working on the machine. Spock very carefully and gently tries to handle him. He explains that McCoy must trust that what he is doing is right and that it is essential that McCoy not engage him in an argument right then. If McCoy says anything at all to upset Spock's frame of mind, it could result in their mission failing and a completely needless war between Vulcan and the Federation; a war that Vulcan would very quickly lose. McCoy is the last person to have any inclination to trust Spock at a time like this, especially the way Spock has been acting. He accuses Spock of hypnotizing Kirk. Spock implores McCoy to trust him and leave him alone for just a few more minutes. McCoy responds to the emotional approach and agrees to leave for the requested time. Spock returns to his meditation.

On board the command starship, the senior officer has briefed Starfleet Command on the events that have occurred. He is awaiting instructions as to what should be done next. Starfleet tells the ships to hold position and to try to convince the Vulcans to allow them to stay in the area in order to search for the Enterprise or its debris. The senior officer contacts the Vulcans again and explains things as per his orders. The Vulcans inform him that they will commence firing in 94 seconds.

On the Enterprise, Spock gets up, plays with a number of buttons and dials, then puts his hand on a plate of the machine as if he were doing a mind meld with it. He keeps it there for what seems a long time. His face is beatific. He removes his hand and swiftly begins fiddling with the control panel of the machine.

Vulcan ship: the commander counts down to firing phasers. He reaches zero and gives the command to fire.

Enterprise: Spock hits a final button.

In orbit over Vulcan, we see the phaser beams shoot out from the Vulcan ships. They get halfway to the Federation ships when all the ships and phaser beams disappear, along with the Vulcan Force Field. A moment later, the Enterprise appears.

Spock, on the bridge again, looks his old self. Kirk, who has lost his pointed ears, wonders if anybody knows what happened. Spock explains that there was no way to retrieve the negative psychic emanations and therefore he had to counteract the cloud by emitting another cloud, a cloud of peaceful, trusting thoughts. Kirk points out that if this is true, then Spock was responsible for the Vulcan people's change from an emotional warlike race into pacifists. Spock tells him that's not exactly true, because once his deed was done, it was as if nothing at all had happened. Kirk's restored ears and Spock's return to normal are proof of that. The events that have transpired will only be true for those on board the Enterprise. Neutralizing the cloud erased the cul-de-sac of time they had traveled from everywhere in the universe except their memories. Kirk calls the mission complete and asks if Spock would like to be dropped off on Vulcan before he takes the Enterprise home. Spock would just as soon experience Earth for awhile. As he turns away, we see a touch of the human gleam in his eye and a smile plays around the corners of his mouth.

Fade Out – The End.

Comparatively speaking, one of the more interesting aspects of this story idea was Spock bringing his human half to the surface, and behaving like a fully emotional being for one of the first times. This mirrors the development of Data, the android science officer aboard the Enterprise-D in *Star Trek: The Next Generation* who, after installing an emotion chip within the course of the feature film *Star Trek: Generations*, went through a similar emotional display.

Jon Povill, who would eventually go on to be story editor of the proposed *Star Trek II* television series and associate producer of the first feature film, had worked with Gene Roddenberry as a researcher for what was then planned to be a novelization of *The God Thing*.

"Gene went to work on *The God Thing* in May of 1975," says Povill. "By August the script was turned down. Gene suggested I do a treatment for a film, which I did. Gene read it and said, 'It would make a nice episode, but it's not a feature.' Then in December he called me and said, 'I have another idea for a feature, would you like to come in and help me write the treatment?' In January I moved into my office and started working on the treatment."

STAR TREK II (1975)

A darkened and lifeless Enterprise is suspended in blackness. Beneath the vessel is an "eerie luminescence" that turns out to be a mass of pulsating crystal plasma. According to the description in the treatment, "it defies the notions of surface or border, creating a sweeping vista of phosphorescent color and form in ever-changing patterns."

Within the plasma are the mangled, and apparently lifeless, bodies of Kirk and the rest of the Enterprise crew. Then, miraculously, the bodies begin to heal and slowly disappear, only to rematerialize on the Enterprise which has also come back to its own form of life. Kirk appears in the command chair, clearly remembering the sensation of having died.

In an attempt to more fully understand what has happened, Kirk has ship log tapes played back. Through them we learn that the Enterprise has been studying a black hole. Spock, Scotty and a 12-member science team, utilizing a science pod, jettisoned from the great vessel to study the phenomena at a varying proximity. A sudden surge of energy which collapsed toward the center of the black hole also managed to capture the Enterprise in its wake. What happened next, they assume, is that the vessel and her crew met their demise.

Kirk has McCoy begin examinations to determine if they actually had died, while ordering Uhura to raise Starfleet Command. Static is their only response. Chekov compounds the bad news by announcing that they are so far away from their own galaxy that they cannot begin to determine their location. To make matters worse, even at maximum warp it would take over a century for them to reach their own galaxy (sounds like the premise of the syndicated series *Star Trek: Voyager*).

The captain has the energy mass outside the ship scanned in the hope that it might be some kind of life form. Unfortunately there is no response, but, when he attempts to beam into it, Kirk finds himself back in his command chair. "The mass does have a will," he surmises. "It must be alive."

The final members of the crew have materialized, but, by their absence, it seems that Spock, Scott and the science party are lost forever. The mass abruptly disappears and Enterprise effortlessly achieves warp nine. Full ship scans indicate that somehow every aspect of the vessel has been dramatically improved to go somewhere. But where? And why?

Once they approach their own galaxy, thanks to the ship's improved power, Chekov is able to determine that they had been dead for eleven years. Control of the helm is restored, and Kirk orders the ship to head for Starbase 12. They are shocked to find that there is no trace of the starbase.

Enroute to Earth, they encounter a Rigelian starship, whose captain does not recognize the Enterprise and informs Kirk that Earth has never been a part of the Federation of Planets. In the ensuing battle, Enterprise manages to disable the Rigelian ship.

Growing more confused by the moment, Kirk retires to his quarters, contemplating the words of the Rigelian and pondering the fate of Spock. Should they divert to Vulcan to see if he is there? McCoy had suggested they proceed straight to Earth and, reluctantly, Kirk agreed.

On Vulcan, Spock, in a meditative state, softly utters "Jim?" He becomes troubled by memories of his former life, particularly strange is that he has not had such thoughts in over two years.

Returning to the bridge, Kirk has a course laid in for Vulcan. McCoy feels that this is ill-advised, but the captain points out that there had occasionally been a telepathic link between himself and Spock and, for this reason, Kirk seriously believes that his friend is still alive. More importantly, Spock may hold some clue as to what had happened to them.

They lock into Vulcan orbit, locate Spock and Kirk beams down to his cell-like quarters. Despite the fact he has such a difficult time with emotion, Spock smiles and is genuinely pleased to see his old friend. They beam aboard the Enterprise, which breaks orbit and outraces a squadron of Vulcan cruisers.

Both Kirk and Spock attempt to figure out exactly what is going on. They realize that somehow their universe has been altered, and, judging by the ship's increased speed capabilities, Spock deduces that their mission, whatever that may be, will have something to do with traveling through time. He adds that their task had been to study the black hole phenomena and "compare their distortions to a 'time gap' that Spock had discovered when making an improvement to the transporter system six months before entering the black hole."

The theory is that somehow time has shifted, which is why no one recognizes Enterprise or Spock, and there has never been any contact between Earth and Vulcan. If this theory is correct, Kirk wonders aloud, how did Spock survive? According to the Vulcan, the transporter created a "tiny" time gap when individuals beamed to and from planets, thus protecting them from time shifts.

When they arrive on Earth, there is absolutely no sign of Starfleet Command. "Futuristic design fills the screen awesomely. To our audience the city is a marvel. To Kirk, however, it is a travesty." The city is nothing as it had been. The people are uniformly dressed and the city itself is a conglomeration of structures, lacking the beauty of the 23rd Century they had known.

They go to a library to study history tapes, but after they reveal that they have no authorization, ten large men in white coats approach and begin to beat them. Spock manages to contact the ship, and is able to have himself and Kirk beamed aboard. Meanwhile Uhura has constantly been sending a signal to Earth on Starfleet frequencies, and finally receives a faint response. It is from the survivors of the science pod crew, which validates Spock's theory regarding the immunity to time shifts.

Beaming down to the wilderness locale of the scientists, Kirk and Spock are informed that shortly after they arrived on Earth, the planet's surface was "instantaneously" covered with a vast, ugly urban sprawl. The world was suddenly populated by "a race of mindless automatons who do nothing but eat, sleep and perform their designated functions within the social order." They ask where Scotty is, and are told that he had been working in a special laboratory in Munich, studying the time gap in the transporter so that he could go back in time before their encounter with the black hole and warn Kirk to avoid it. That was the last anyone had heard from him before the changes took place. All of them beam aboard the Enterprise, where they theorize that Scotty himself might have been the source of the time shift.

Kirk, Spock and a security team beam back down to the library, steal computer tapes and beam back up. Spock begins to study them, and learns, at least in theory, that they must go to 1964 Earth and stop Scott from altering history. The trip is successful, but ship's power has been drained quite a bit. If they go back much farther, they will be unable to travel back to the future.

Adorned in appropriate clothing for the time period, Kirk, Spock and Yeoman Roberts (who will recognize the laboratory) beam down to a Munich that "looks notably different than what they expected." Cars have electric motors, people's clothing differ slightly and the whole pace and tone of the city is slower than they expected, thus illustrating that some alterations have already taken place. They discover a replica monument of the laboratory they seek, commemorating the initial appearance of the Mediator in 1937. They are 27 years too late, and it would seem that Scotty has altered history to an incredible degree.

According to people they question, the Mediator brought peace and optimism to the world, cured diseases and fed the hungry. He can be found at the League of Nations headquarters in Geneva. The latter is quite a shock, as it means that World War II never took place.

They beam over to Geneva, only to discover that the Mediator is a computer which was reportedly a gift from aliens who left instructions on how to build it. The work itself was done by a committee of world leaders and scientists.

Kirk meets with Winston Churchill, who denies him access to Montgomery Scott. With little choice, they go back to the Enterprise where they decide to beam the committee aboard so that they can explain their position. Moments later, they beam up, much to their own amazement, Mao Tse Tung, Albert Einstein, John F. Kennedy, Eleanor Roosevelt and two secretaries, who are all overwhelmed to be there. Kirk conducts a tour, ultimately explaining that this is Montgomery Scott's home and he must be returned to it. They have no objections, but only the computer has a direct communication with him.

Using computer tapes as evidence, Kirk goes before the committee, pleading for the opportunity to meet with Scott. Adolph Hitler argues that he is needed here, and, given the fact that Scott is now an old man, he can be of no use to the Enterprise. Hitler is suspicious, pointing out that Kirk would not have "made such a perilous journey simply to renew an old friendship." He demands to know Kirk's true motives. The captain finally explains that Scott is responsible for the future, and has no choice but to show history tapes of what *should* have occurred between the years 1937 and 1964. They witness World War II, use of the atomic bomb, the Korean War, Kennedy's assassination and so forth. They're horrified by what unfolds.

"Granted that this is an awful prospect," says Kirk, "but progress must be made one step at a time by a great number of individuals. Mankind will finally correct these horrors on his own, without the intervention of a 'Mediator.'"

He adds that their Mediator is a product of the history he has wiped out. Because of Scott's interference, the committee has made themselves slaves to a computer. The only way to prevent the world from being enslaved is to allow Kirk to meet with Scott. They refuse, pointing out that they will not allow their age of splendor to become like the one they saw on the viewing screen. Later, and in private, Kennedy tells Kirk that he agrees with him, and, despite the fact a time alteration would claim millions of lives, including his own, gives him the location of Scott's island hideaway in the South Pacific.

Upon reaching the island and overcoming guards, Kirk, Spock and McCoy go to a beautiful palace where they meet with a considerably older Scotty, a man who "has grown accustomed to great power. His bearing is dignified and wise." He quickly recovers from his shock at seeing the trio and explains that his first experiments proved successful. Five years later, he attempted time travel to prevent the black hole incident, but something went wrong and he suddenly found himself surrounded by German soldiers, who immediately attacked him. He was forced to stun them with his phaser.

He merely wanted to return home, but found himself in the position of having to trade scientific information for food and equipment, and, as a result, changes in history were immediately put into effect, most notably the fact that the world's arsenal was more powerful than it should have been at the time. Feeling intense obligation, he had to make sure those weapons were never used.

As time went on, he realized history had already been changed, so all he could do was hope that all the changes would be for the better. Following through with this, he developed potent medicines and agricultural systems, saving lives and eliminating famine. Kirk tells him about the future and Scotty, rather than feeling regret, explains that he could use this knowledge to alter even that time period. Spock disagrees, stating that they need the dilithium crystal which "ornaments Scott's dining table" so that they can return to 1937 and correct history. Scotty will not go, stating that this is his world now, but he gives Kirk the crystal, reasoning that even if the captain straightens everything out,

perhaps this alternate reality will exist on another dimensional plane.

They beam back aboard, and begin their journey. Unfortunately Enterprise's engines will only take them as far back as 1940. Phasers lash out and destroy the specified targets in both Geneva and Munich. A moment later, the Enterprise itself explodes.

A younger and happier Kirk, Spock and Scott appear at Starfleet Command in the proper time frame of the 23rd Century. Spock informs the Command Officer that his time gap calculations were mistaken, and investigation of the black hole will not be necessary.

The Enterprise crew has been rewarded by the alien entity from the outset of the story with another chance at life.

* * *

This scenario was certainly an interesting one, and, if properly handled and developed, would have made a terrific feature film debut for

Star Trek. Both the direction, and the ideas presented are sound and literate. Plus, actor James Doohan would have undoubtedly relished the opportunity to play Scotty on a level that pretty much equaled Kirk and Spock's.

The only complaint regarding this treatment is the lack of definition of just who or what this alien entity is. An earlier draft suggested that this force was actually the combined essence of the humanity which had been wiped from existence as a result of the time alteration, which was a fascinating turn of events.

In the early 1980s there was a rumor that Gene Roddenberry had written a sequel to Star Trek: The Motion Picture in which the Enterprise prevented the assassination of President Kennedy and, as a result, all history was changed. Spock supposedly had to fire a deadly phaser beam at the president to set history back on course. It would seem highly likely that those rumors were based on this treatment.

THE BILLION YEAR VOYAGE

After Paramount Pictures had rejected the Gene Rodden-berry-Jon Povill treatment for *Star Trek II*, the studio began interviewing writers on their own, attempting to find the proper one to handle the project. Their attempts were fruitless.

Nonetheless, it's still interesting to take a look at exactly who they had been speaking to. Reportedly, innumerable writers came in to pitch story ideas, and among those the most recognizable to genre fans were John D.F. Black, who had served as story editor of the first season of *Star Trek* and had written "The Naked Time," famed author – Harlan Ellison, whose sole contribution to the show had been the highly acclaimed "City on the Edge of Forever," and science fiction veteran Robert Silverberg.

John D.F. Black describes the storyline he pitched with a good natured shrug. Something in his voice conveys the feeling that he still can't believe the way the studio had been handling the film. "I came up with a story concept involving a black hole," recounts Black, "and this was before Disney's film. The black hole had been used by several planets in a given constellation as a garbage dump. But with a black hole there's a point of equality. In other words, when enough positive matter comes into contact with an equal amount of negative matter, the damn thing blows up. Well if that ever occurs with a black hole, it's the end of the universe – it'll swallow everything. What I saw was that the Enterprise discovers what's happening with this particular black hole and they try to stop these planets from unloading into it. The planets won't do it. It comes to war in some areas and, as a result, the black hole comes to balance and blows up. At that point, it would continue to chew up matter.

In 106 years Earth would be swallowed by this black hole, and the Enterprise is trying to beat the end of the world. There were at least twenty sequels in that story because the jeopardy keeps growing more intense."

Paramount rejected the idea. "They said it wasn't big enough," he notes wryly.

In his excellent nonfiction assessment of horror and science fiction, *Danse Macabre*, Stephen King reported that rumor had it Harlan Ellison had gone to Paramount and found them looking for a "big" idea for a *Star Trek* film. According to this rumor, Ellison had the Enterprise break through the end of the universe and confront God himself.

They thought that wasn't big enough.

Removing tongue from cheek, the author explained the real story to King, but before that explanation, it will be of interest to note what James Van Hise, the editor of the *Star Trek* fanzine *Enterprise Incidents,* had to say about the Ellison story pitch.

"The story Harlan came up with," Van Hise wrote in issue eight of his magazine, "was never written down but was presented verbally. The story did not begin with any of the Enterprise crew, but started on Earth where strange phenomenon were inexplicably occurring. In India, a building where a family is having dinner just vanishes into dust. In the United States, one of the Great Lakes suddenly vanishes, wreaking havoc. In a public square, a woman suddenly screams and falls to the pavement where she transforms into some sort of reptilian creature. The truth is suppressed, but the Federation realizes that someone or something is tampering with time and changing things on Earth in the far distant past. What is actually happening involves an alien race on the other side of the galaxy. Eons ago, Earth and this planet both developed races of humans and intelligent humanoid

reptiles. On Earth, the humans destroyed the reptile men and flourished, but on the other world the opposite occurred and when the reptilian race learns what happened on Earth in the remote past, they decide to change things in the past so that they will have a kindred planet. For whatever reason, the Federation decides that only the Enterprise and her crew are qualified for this mission, so a mysterious cloaked figure goes about kidnapping the old central crew. This figure is finally revealed to be Kirk. After they are reunited, they prepare for the mission into the past to save Earth. And that would have been just the first half hour of the film!"

Ellison gave Stephen King a little more information on his story meeting with Paramount.

"It involved going to the end of the known universe to slip back through time to the Pleistocene period when man first emerged," he said. "I postulated a parallel development of reptile life that might have developed into the dominant species on Earth had not mammals prevailed. I postulated an alien intelligence from a far galaxy where the snakes *had* become the dominant life form, and a snake-creature who had come to Earth in the *Star Trek* future, had seen its ancestors wiped out, and had gone back into the far past of Earth to set up distortions in the timeflow so the reptiles could beat the humans. The Enterprise goes back to set time right, finds the snake-alien, and the human crew is confronted with the moral dilemma of whether it had the right to wipe out an entire life form just to insure its own territorial imperative in our present and future. The story, in short, spanned all of time and all of space, with a moral and ethical problem."

Paramount executive Barry Trabulus "listened to all this and sat silently for a few minutes," Ellison elaborated. "Then he said, 'You know, I was reading this book by a guy named Von Daniken and he proved that the Mayan calendar was exactly like ours, so it must have come from aliens. Could you put in some Mayans?'"

The writer pointed out that there were no Mayans at the dawn of time, but the executive brushed this off, pointing out that no one would know the difference.

"'I'm to know the difference,'" Ellison exploded. "'It's a dumb suggestion.' So Trabulus got very uptight and said he liked Mayans a lot and why didn't I do it if I wanted to write this picture. So I said, 'I'm a writer. I don't know what . . . .you are!' And I got up and walked out. And that was the end of my association with the *Star Trek* movie."

Robert Silverberg's effort for this apparent revolving door at Paramount was entitled *The Billion Year Voyage*, a 51 page treatment that begins with the Enterprise having just completed a mission on Persis, where the inhabitants are telepathically linked together to form a single "super-entity."

Staring into space, Kirk comments to Spock on the vastness of space, adding that the distance between galaxies can't compare to that which separates one being from another. "We are each alone," Silverberg notes, "isolated, prisoners in our skulls, doing our best to reach the souls of others, and our best, the Captain says, is never good enough. Can we ever truly know another person? Can we ever actually trust anyone? Can we really touch someone else?"

As McCoy joins in on the conversation, Spock states, "The Captain is troubled by the loneliness of the human condition, Doctor."

Kirk admits the sociological structure of Persis is not what he has in mind, but he does wish that there were a way to truly reach someone; to achieve a communion of a kind. Spock, he considers, with the Vulcan mind-meld has actually achieved that which he finds himself seeking.

Spock is uncomfortable with this whole line of conversation, and it takes McCoy to make Kirk recognize this.

As the treatment notes, "This opening interchange establishes Kirk (romantic, impulsive, sensitive, struggling in an almost inarticulate way to transcend his limitations); Spock (coldly logical, repressing all show of emotion, yet clearly subject to turbulent flows of humanity deep within himself which he feels he must keep in check); and McCoy (flippant, sardonic, but wise and perceptive). The scene also establishes one of the central themes to be resolved at the climax of the movie: the spiritual isolation of a non-telepathic species, each mind locked away from all others by impenetrable barriers."

At that moment, Uhura picks up an emergency from a group of archeologists on Aurora V, who have been excavating a Great Ones occupation site.

Silverberg detailed some background information on the Great Ones sites. Thus far there have been 23 discovered over the past 12 years over a thousand light-years. Each of these sites follow a particular pattern: they are seemingly outposts as opposed to settlements; similar artifacts are found at every site – intricate, baffling objects of gold and plastic, their craftsmanship being superb; and dating techniques have determined them to be anywhere from 850 million to one billion years. "Which means," he wrote, "the Great Ones had developed a galactic civilization at a time when nothing more than complex trilobites had evolved on Earth, and that their culture had changed very little during a span of at least a quarter of a billion years – implying a rigid, conservative civilization enduring for a period of time beyond human comprehension. Archeological teams are searching the galaxy for the Great Ones' homeworld."

Uhura reports that the team is

threatened by so-called invisible enemies. A skeptical Kirk wants her to have a smaller ship in that quadrant investigate, but Spock argues – passionately – that they should investigate. McCoy suggests they investigate, pointing out privately that Spock has become extremely fascinated by the Great Ones. As they are on a routine patrol, Kirk agrees and has the Enterprise alter course for Aurora V.

Once there, Spock, Chekov and Yeoman Baker (an American Indian woman) beam down and meet with the archeologists, including leaders Dr. Henry Justinian, Dr. Hrkk of Fff and Pilazool of Shilamak, "a walking, talking machine man with nothing much left that's organic except his brain."

Spock requests that they be taken to the Great Ones site immediately, without even mentioning the distress signal. It is Chekov who brings it up, to which archeologist Kelley responds that things have mysteriously disappeared and they've heard ghostly footsteps. They fear that the site is haunted. Spock, naturally, is skeptical. "Gifted," Kelley claims she can detect a psychic aura from the intruder telepathically. The presence of others she detects have overtones of cruelty, treachery and unscrupulousness. Spock muses that she must be talking about Klingons, to which Kelley agrees. It is possible, she points out, that the Klingons may have discovered Great Ones sites as well. It's her feeling that the Klingons may have discovered a Great Ones device to render them invisible and that they may be hovering around the site at this moment.

When Kelley is called away, Spock, Chekov and Baker start exploring the site. Baker is abruptly grabbed by an invisible hand and carried away. A moment later, Chekov notices she's missing and informs Spock. Both men are attacked. Using his acute hearing, Spock is able to detect the location of their opponents and wards them off. Kelley and other members of the archeologist team arrive. Spock contacts the Enterprise to tell Kirk that there are indeed invisible beings lurking there. It's his suggestion that the captain send down a search party with thermal sensors so that their heat-energy can be detected. Kirk agrees.

Kirk beams down with a landing party, and there is an instant romantic attraction between him and Kelley. The search begins, and as day becomes night they find Baker, battered but okay. They retire for the night, and the next day two things become obvious: Spock is growing obsessed over the Great Ones, and Kirk is completely infatuated with Kelley, while the excavation of the site continues.

Days pass and all is quiet, until one of the invisible beings lifts a pickax and is about to bring it down on Spock's skull while the Vulcan studies a metal globe that he's found. Kirk and Kelley see this and Kirk fires his phaser. The "invisible" transforms into a dead Klingon. Suddenly they're attacked by a whole group of invisible Klingons. It's a savage battle, but our people are ultimately victorious and the prisoners are beamed up to the Enterprise.

When everything settles down, the group examines the globe found by Spock. It's accidentally dropped and comes to life. "A strange blue light comes from slits along its surface; the field of light widens and grows more dense until it becomes a globe of dense color, large enough to encompass the entire group. A 360-degree holographic projection can be seen, totally surrounding everyone; they are inside it, watching bizarre images take form, pictures congealing out of blue fog. For a long dreamlike moment, no one moves. Then Pilazool, the machine-man, is seen crouching over the globe, frowning, touching the control stud. The images vanish instantly. He touches it again: the globe starts to project. He shuts it off. Excitement."

The images they see are of the Great Ones, six-limbed humanoids described as having a reptilian ancestry; then of their cities; and, finally, "a cave interior, walls encrusted with glistening crystals. The camera looks through the transparent floor of the cave to see colossal machines throbbing and hammering in an underground chamber: huge green pistons pumping endlessly, sleek black conveyor belts, spinning turbines."

The globe is shut off and it's obvious that the watchers are awed by what they've seen. Later, McCoy beams down just in time to see a new image being projected by the globe. They see a Great Ones ship moving through space, orbiting a very distinctive asteroid and releasing a series of robots which carve – out of the asteroid – a vault, in which one robot is left behind. When the images are over, Kirk muses over the possibility of a Great One robot being somewhere on this planet in a vault. Spock believes, given the obvious durability of the race's technology, that is indeed a possibility. If the Klingons are staking out Great Ones sites, Kirk reasons, it's vital that the Federation stay one jump ahead of them. They will seek out this asteroid.

The archeologist team joins Kirk and the others as they beam back aboard the Enterprise. Feeding all known information into the ship's computers, they come to the conclusion that the asteroid they seek is in their own galaxy. Utilizing computer simulation of the galaxy as it looked a billion years ago, Spock is able to discern the proper star pattern they need. The locale is Gamma 1443, and that's where they're headed.

According to the treatment, "what Kirk doesn't know is that several invisible Klingons have stowed away on the Enterprise. Their presence is made known to the audience, but not to any member of Kirk's command. Kelley's telepathic powers are of no value in detecting these stowaways, since she is picking up Klingon aura anyway from the prisoners in the brig and has no way of knowing that additional Klingons are prowling the ship."

They reach Gamma 1443, which is supposedly so close to death that it emits only a trickle of light. The star's temperature is 980 degrees, too hot for a landing but far too feeble to sustain a solar system. Enterprise locks into orbit around an asteroid belt and begins the search for the right one. After much searching, the proper asteroid is found. Kirk leads a landing party to the vault. The door is opened and one of the scientists, Dr. Hrkkk, rushes in, but is incinerated by a blinding yellow light. The Great Ones machinery is still operating, obviously, and remains guarded by the robot which has survived the passage of time.

Kirk has the globe beamed down and turns it on, its images flooding the vault. The robot responds, standing to its full height of 12-feet, and takes the globe from Kirk. The robot turns the globe on, watches the vault construction scene and points to the pattern of projected stars, indicating the very different present-day pattern.

"It's telling us it knows a lot of time has passed," says McCoy.

From there, the robot beckons them to follow it into the vault. The incinerator turned off, they agree. The robot shows them "a kind of travelogue of the Great Ones' civilization."

Notes McCoy, "They make our accomplishments look like the doings of monkeys in a tree."

"And yet," Kirk counters, "monkeys though we are, we've managed to find our way across the universe to this place and set their robot free. Not bad ... for monkeys."

Enterprise computers are able to translate the robot's language, and the robot, in turn, begins speaking in English. We learn that the robot – who they've nicknamed Ozymandias, is awaiting the return of the Great

Ones. When asked about the home-world of the Great Ones, Ozymandias, fearing for the safety of its creators, stops talking and retreats to the vault, switching the defensive field back on.

Kelley claims that the robot has a mind, and it's her thought that she could make herself a conduit between Kirk and the robot, "to set up a telepathic patch linking them so that Ozymandias can perceive Kirk's mind and reassure itself about the Captain's intentions. Kirk is immediately enthusiastic."

There are drawbacks, she notes. Primary among them is that if there is an imbalance, Kirk's mind could be burned out, though this doesn't seem a likely possibility. After Spock and McCoy voice their protests, Kirk asks her whether or not there would be any way to avoid such a reaction. Kelley muses that she could possibly link two minds to the robot so that there would be enough "mental energy" to handle any kind of a sudden surge. McCoy agrees to take part in this. Kelley begins, but Kirk passes out and we learn that Spock, sensing that the mind-link was too strong even for the combination of Kirk-McCoy, took their place. Moments later, Spock comes out of it and Ozymandias agrees to show them the homeworld of its creators.

Ozymandias peers into space and appears as confused as a robot can appear to be. He claims that the proper star isn't there. It's gone. The robot asks them to help it by bringing it to a nearby solar system where the Great Ones had established a large colony.

Everyone boards the Enterprise and makes way for McBurney's Star at warp factor three. Enroute, Kelley informs Kirk that she has received a mental message from her brother. Science Command wants her back on Aurora V. Kirk refers to Spock and McCoy. The Vulcan states that he should obey the orders, while the doctor argues that Kirk should do what's right for the Enterprise and Starfleet. Since he's not under Science Command's jurisdiction. Kelley wants to stay aboard, so the starship continues on its journey.

On McBurney IV, sensors detect a living city in terms of machinery, but there are no organic lifeforms down there. Ozymandias contacts fellow robots on the planet's surface, and at that moment all power drains from the Enterprise, the starship snared by the planet's gravity. Kirk is about to give the abandon ship order, when Scotty announces that the Enterprise "doesn't seem to be accelerating as it hurtles planetward. It is drifting down, floating, feather-light – as though in the grip of some titanic force. It violates all the laws of physics. The atmospheric molecules themselves are opening before the starship to provide it with a friction-free vacuum chute." Enterprise touches down, gently.

The robots which gather around them are fascinated, as they've never seen living beings before. They are machines which were created by machines. Shortly thereafter, Ozymandias announces that the Great Ones perished some 84,005,675 years earlier, leaving only their machines behind. It adds that the homeworld does exist but it is part of a Dyson sphere.

Silverberg details, "Dyson spheres were conceived by the 20th Century physicist Freeman Dyson, who observed that a solar system is a terribly wasteful thing. The central sun throws most of its energy into space; only air action is intercepted and used by the planets that surround it. A truly thrifty civilization would demolish one large uninhabited planet and use its mass to build a shell enclosing the sun at a distance of several hundred million miles. This would intercept every photon of energy the sun emitted. The builders would leave their native planet and take up residence on the inner surface of the artificial sphere. Not only would every point on that surface have constant access to sunlight, but the surface area of the sphere would be a billion times greater than the area of Earth, supporting an immensely expanded population with no energy problems whatsoever. A Dyson sphere, of course, would not show up on optical telescopes, since all of the sun's light output is trapped within the sphere. Which is why Ozymandias was unable to find it with an optical scan. It would however radiate its surplus heat in the infrared wavelengths, and could easily be detected that way."

Enterprise proceeds back to the homeworld of the Great Ones. Enroute, it starts to become apparent that something mysterious is happening on board the Enterprise, though no one suspects invisible Klingons. Shortly thereafter, the ship is in orbit around the shell of the home world

While Ozymandias attempts to contact its creators, three Klingon battlecruisers launch an attack while, simultaneously, the invisible Klingons enter the Enterprise's phaser room, overpower the crew and disable the ship's weapon systems.

As Enterprise shields are buffeted, Spock and Kelley are able to launch an attack against the invisible Klingons. Ozymandias proceeds to the bridge and offers assistance. At first Kirk is reluctant to trust a machine, but he realizes it may be the only solution. Ozymandias hooks itself up to the ship's computer, and provides Enterprise with the edge it needs to prove victorious in this battle. The battle over, Ozymandias makes contact and a portion of the sphere opens to allow Enterprise to enter. As the vessel approaches a landing area, Ozymandias tells Kirk that 4,852 Great Ones still survive.

The landing party meets with a Great One, with life support equipment hooked up to various parts of its body. The being is described as "hideously old. Its body is wrinkled and pouchy; its scales no longer overlap, but spread apart to reveal folds of soft grayish skin. The eyes are dull, the expression slack. It does not move. It shows no sign that it is aware of them. It seems barely alive."

Ozymandias explains that they are all like that and will more than likely remain that way. It's Kirk's feeling that they should move on, that "it" deserves some privacy. As they walk off, they find a variety of Great One artifacts, including a thought amplifier, which permits communication from one mind to another. Kirk is intrigued with the notion of trying the device, but Spock is put off by the idea. The Vulcan mind-meld is a highly personal joining of the mind and is used only under the most extreme circumstances. Otherwise it is an invasion of privacy.

As the group steps into the corridor, Ozymandias announces that he must meet with his creators. While the Enterprise personnel await his return, Kirk is knocked down by an invisible foe, and the battle begins anew between our people and the Klingons, who have somehow escaped from the brig. Kelley, under great strain, begins picking up the Klingon auras and points them out for the others. But it proves too much for her. Kelley collapses, and the Klingons start to

gain the upper hand. Out of desperation, Kirk places the Great Ones thought amplifier on his head, resulting in "an electric effect. He reacts as though a spike has been jammed into his skull. But only for a moment. The pain and surprise recede. Kirk is having a transcendental experience. He is *touching other minds.*"

A smile crosses his lips as he reads the thoughts of McCoy, Scotty and Spock. Additionally, he is able to read the Klingons as well. With hardly any effort, he locates the Klingons, pulls them away from the others and phasers them. The dead Klingons materialize. Everyone is shocked at what he was able to do, and he tries to reassure them, ecstatic at being able to touch the minds of others. Only then does he remember that Kelley had collapsed.

Enterprise: In sickbay, McCoy tells Kirk that Kelley will be okay. Her eyes open shortly thereafter, and Kirk tells her that everything will be alright, though he's saddened by the realization that she'll be heading back to Earth and they'll probably never see each other again.

As Kirk leaves sickbay, he finds Spock in the corridor, holding a Great Ones thought amplifier in his hands. He is concerned over the impact that

this device, as well as others from the Great Ones, will have on a civilization as relatively primitive as ours. It's his suggestion that it would be more logical to declare the Great Ones' homeworld off limits to all beings, and that vessels be posted to guard the planet. Kirk says he'll report to Starfleet and let them make the final decision. "What do you think will happen?" McCoy asks.

"I imagine," muses Kirk, "we'll make use of whatever we can handle at this stage of our development, and put the rest away until the proper time. At least, that's what I hope they'll do."

Whatever they decide, Kirk has had a brief taste of the communal mind, and feels that he'll never be the same again.

With that, the Enterprise departs the Great Ones' homeworld to begin its next adventure.

* * *

There's some wonderful build up here that doesn't pay off at the ending. Silverberg introduces some marvelous concepts, but as a whole it's understandable why this one didn't make it to the screen.

STAR TREK: THE MOTION PICTURE (1976)

This 1976 version was slated to be directed by Philip Kaufman and scripted by Allan Scott and Chris Bryant.

The screenplay opens with the Enterprise investigating a distress signal sent from the U.S.S. DaVinci. By the time they arrive in that quadrant of space, the other starship is gone. Suddenly, Kirk's brain is struck by electromagnetic waves, which results in erratic behavior and his commandeering a shuttlecraft. He pilots it towards an invisible planet and disappears. Three years later, Spock leads an expedition back to that area of space, and they discover what they believe to be the planet of the Titans, an ancient but highly advanced race which had been thought extinct. Problem is that the planet is being drawn towards a black hole, and it becomes a race against time between the Federation and the Klingons, who are both interested in that particular world. The one who saves the planet will receive the fruits of their knowledge.

On the planet's surface, Spock discovers Kirk, who has been living there as a wild man. The captain is restored to normal in short order, and together they discover that the planet is actually populated by the evil Cygnans, a race which had destroyed the Titans. The story concluded with Kirk, in an effort to destroy the hostile Cygnans, ordering the Enterprise into the black hole. As Susan Sackett noted in *The Making of Star Trek: The Motion Picture*, "During the trip through the black hole, the Cygnans are destroyed and the Enterprise emerges in orbit around Earth. But it is the Earth at the time of the Cro-Magnon man, the dawn of humanity. The Titans, it would seem, were the men of the Enterprise."

Jon Povill recalls, "It was an interesting script in a certain sort of way. It was not *Star Trek*. People would have gone to see it and it would have done as well as we did with *Star Trek: The Motion Picture*, but it's just as well it didn't get made. Chris and Allan even felt that it was something that wasn't quite successful."

STAR TREK II
THE TELEVISION SERIES
(1977–78)

While America is on the verge of celebrating *Star Trek*'s 30th Anniversary, it seems difficult to believe that the return of the show had taken so long to accomplish.

There had been numerous attempts to recreate the voyages of the starship Enterprise, but none seemed as certain as the proposed syndicated series, *Star Trek II*. This show was announced in June 1977, one month after the theatrical release of *Star Wars*, and shut down one week before production began in November of that same year. The original cast – except Leonard Nimoy, who, for a variety of reasons, did not wish to portray Mr. Spock again in a weekly series – had actually been signed to reprise their roles; scripts were being developed and sets constructed. Everything was coming together for *Star Trek* to touch a new generation.

For some time, Barry Diller, then the head of Paramount Pictures, had dreamed of starting a fourth television network to compete with the three majors (a dream Diller would realize with Fox Broadcasting a decade later). To this end, Paramount contacted independent stations throughout the United States and began offering product to fill one night a week, cornerstoned by *Star Trek II*.

Robert Goodwin, assistant to Paramount Executive Arthur Fellows and current co-executive producer of *The X-Files*, was hired as the Director of Development for the company's latest acquisition, Playboy Enterprises. He remained in that position for about a year.

"Then, Gary Nardino came in and took over as President of Para-mount Television, and made the decision to start a fourth network," Goodwin details. "The plan was that every Saturday night, they were going to do one hour of Star Trek and a two-hour movie. My interest had always been more in the long form rather than the series side of television. Nardino decided that he was going to put me in charge of all these two-hour movies, which was great for me."

At that point, forces were at work which would pull Goodwin away from his choice assignment and transfer him to the *Star Trek* offices. Meanwhile, Gene Roddenberry grew more excited with each passing day. His seemingly unending battle to bring *Star Trek* back had apparently come to an end, and he essentially had an opportunity to surpass himself, although he never really looked at it that way.

"Those [original] episodes will always be there for what people want to make out of them," Roddenberry said at the time. "We're making a new set of them 10 years later under very different circumstances. Neither takes away from the other. The worst that can happen is someone would say that Roddenberry couldn't do it a second time. That doesn't bother me, as long as I did my damndest to do it a second time."

Star Trek II was deemed a unique project for those involved, and efforts were made to secure the proper creative team. Robert Goodwin was first choice as a producer.

"They were looking for someone to come on as producer," recalls Goodwin, "and Gene Roddenberry had heard about me. To be perfectly honest, I wasn't anxious to do it. My real interest was the long form, all those two-hour movies. I was pretty much strong-armed to do the show and not given too much of a choice. Paramount said, 'Forget the movies, you're doing *Star Trek*.' To make a long story short, [Roddenberry] wanted me to go in as one of two producers. They were going to hire a writing producer and a production producer. It was a strange situation."

Roddenberry found his "writing producer" in Harold Livingston, a novelist and TV writer who would go on to write *Star Trek: The Motion Picture*.

"I had never paid much attention to *Star Trek*," Livingston smiles sheepishly. "I had always considered it something of a media event. I was *totally* unwashed. But I wanted to make it more universal. I felt that *Star Trek*, its success not withstanding, had a restrictive audience. There was a greater audience for it and my broad intention was to create a series that would attract a larger audience by offering *more*. We would still offer the same elements as the original *Star Trek*, i.e. science fiction and hope for the future, and then do realistic stories.

"I just thought they had reached a certain barrier with it. How much could you do before it becomes totally redundant? They had so many stories which, to manipulate or move the plot, this goofy thing appeared out of nowhere. I'm thinking specifically of some Greek with an echoing voice that came on at the end and saved them. That was done too often. I wanted scripts that were interesting, made sense and moved from a literary standpoint. Anyway, thirteen episodes plus a pilot were ordered, and it was then my job to develop these stories, which I set upon doing."

To this end, he enlisted the aid of Jon Povill, Gene Roddenberry's assistant, who would become the proposed series' story editor and associate producer of ST:TMP.

"Harold wasn't very familiar with the old series at all," says Povill, "and relied on me to be the monitor of whether something fit with Star Trek or not. Once everything got rolling, and we were in many writers' meetings, I took over as the person who pointed out where there were holes in the stories, and where they didn't conform to what Star Trek was supposed to be."

Rounding out the early behind-the-scenes personnel was Jim Rugg, a veteran from the original series, who was to handle the special effects; and Joe Jennings, who was signed as production designer.

"The Enterprise's bridge," explains Jennings, "was designed to go into series, so we were designing it to be all things to all people. As a result, all of the devices were practical and worked off proximity switches. You don't have to touch the board, but simply had to reach toward it and whatever effect you were tripping would show up on the board. We were asked to design a set that would function for at least three years of shows, so we were being much more sophisticated than perhaps we would have been were it just a feature film. Then, you only build things that operate properly."

While behind-the-scenes production began to take shape, scripts were being written to accommodate the absence of Mr. Spock. Filling this void were new characters: Lieutenant Xon, a full Vulcan serving as Enterprise Science Officer, who would have a certain "legend" to live up to; Commander Will Decker, son of Commodore Matt Decker, who met his demise on the original series' "Doomsday Machine" episode, as

First Officer; and the bald Lieutenant Ilia, the passionate Deltan navigator with empathic abilities.

Decker and Ilia would eventually reach the screen in Star Trek: The Motion Picture, although in somewhat altered form. For starters, the film quickly establishes that at one time they were romantically involved with each other, which was not the situation planned for the series. Ilia, for the most part, remained the same, but Decker's attitude was completely different. Through the course of Star Trek II, the audience would have seen a father-son relationship develop between Decker and Kirk, as the young officer would slowly be trained for his own command. Additionally, Decker would have led many of the landing parties, thus leaving Kirk on board the Enterprise to handle the adventure from that vantage point. It's a dramatic device quite similar to the one finally established on Star Trek: The Next Generation, between Captain Jean Luc Picard and Commander William Riker.

"The original series had 78 episodes," Jon Povill notes, "and therefore many things had already been done. The challenge was coming up with things that weren't repeats of ideas already explored. What we were definitely striving for on the show was doing things that were different, and I think by and large we were successful. That was the biggest challenge; coming up with things that were fresh and were also Star Trek.

"The characters of Xon, Decker and Ilia would have helped in this area. We wanted characters who could go in new directions, as well as the old crew. I particularly liked Xon. I thought there was something very fresh in having a nice young Vulcan to deal with; somebody who was trying to live up to a previous image. That, to me, was a very nice gimmick for a TV show that was missing Spock. But we never wanted Xon to be a Spock retread. We wanted him to be some-

body who definitely had his own direction to go in, and he had different failings than Spock. Also, he didn't have Spock's neurosis regarding his human half. As far as Xon was concerned, Spock had a distinct advantage in being half-Vulcan and half-human in the context of where he was, what he was doing and where he was working. If he was on Vulcan, it wouldn't have been an advantage, but to be living with humans, it really helped. Xon's youth was also very important and he would have brought a freshness that people would have appreciated.

"Ilia was sort of an embodiment of warmth, sensuality, sensitivity and a nice Yin to Xon's Yang. Decker, of course, was a young Kirk. I think he would have been the least distinct. He would have had to grow, and the performance probably would have done that, bringing something to Decker that the writers would have ultimately latched on to for material. He's the one who would have to develop more through the acting and performance than the other two. Xon and Ilia were concept characters. They would have developed, too, I'm sure, because characters grow when they're performed much more than they do from just the writing. In the early writing, you don't realize the full potential. You don't know who's going to play the character, how they're going to play it and what the characteristics of their performance are going to be. If you look at 'The Menagerie,' for example, Spock actually laughs."

During pre-production for the series, only the role of Xon was actually cast. Actor David Gautreaux, who would go on to play a V'ger victim, Starbase Epsilon 9's Commander Branch, in ST:TMP, signed aboard as the Enterprise's newest Vulcan.

"When I got the role," explains the actor, "I actually went off on a meditative trek and fasted for ten days. I allowed my hair to grow long. I started researching to be a Vulcan with no emotion. For an actor, that's death. How do you appear as having no emotion without looking like a piece of wood? That was my acting objective.

"In all honesty," Gautreaux continues, "I was looking forward to playing Xon. His actions were tremendous as well as his strength without size and the aspect of playing a full Vulcan. When I say that, I mean a more involved presence on the show and the running of the ship. It was a very exciting premise to be playing. To me, it was a potentially good gig that didn't work out."

While Gautreaux was being cast, scripts had begun coming in and director Bob Collins was signed to helm the two-hour premiere episode. Based on Alan Dean Foster's treatment, "In Thy Image," in which a NASA space probe returns to Earth hundreds of years later, highly metamorphosized and seeking its creator, this story eventually became the basis of *Star Trek: The Motion Picture.*

"At that point," says Robert Goodwin, "they had spent about four years trying to get a script for a feature, but they couldn't come up with anything that Michael Eisner liked. We had various options on the two-hour thing, and I suggested to Gene that since it had never been done in the series before, we should come up with a story in which Earth was threatened. In all the previous *Star Trek* episodes, they never came close to Earth."

"In Thy Image" seemed an answer to Goodwin's prayers. "I remember," he adds, "that one day we went into the administration building. At this big meeting, there was [then-Paramount, now Disney execs] Michael Eisner and Jeff Katzenberg, Gary Nardino, Gene, me and a bunch of other people. In that meeting, I got up and pitched this two-hour story. Eisner slammed his hands on the table and said, 'We've spent four years looking for a feature script. This is it! Now, let's make the movie.'"

The transformation of the *Star Trek II* series into a film came about for several reasons. First, the proposed Paramount Network had been unable to sell enough advertising time to compete with the established TV networks. Second, not only had *Star Wars* been released and become an unprecedented phenomenon, but Steven Spielberg's *Close Encounters of the Third Kind* had achieved box office success as well, thus proving that science fiction had a place on the motion picture screen.

"When 'In Thy Image' became a feature," explains director Bob Collins, "we were given a budget of about $8 million. Somewhere around that time, we were talking about special effects. *Close Encounters* was about to open, and the word around town was that it was spectacular. So, Roddenberry and I went down to the Pacific Theatre and sat down for what I think was a noon performance. We came out, both pretty blown away. I turned to him and said, 'Well, there goes our low budget special effects.' After *Star Wars* and *Close Encounters*, you couldn't do low budget special effects anymore. That meant a whole new way of thinking and a whole re-organization of the production and concepts. They needed a great deal more money and time, and there were only a few people who could do it."

The budget eventually reached $20 million, and at that point Collins began to suspect that his days with the project were numbered.

"We were preparing to make this picture," he says, "but the writing was on the wall. I was a television director who hadn't done a feature film at that time. It was evident that they were going to hire somebody who *had* done a feature and was used to working with big budget special effects. Paramount wasn't brave about such things, so I called up Jeff Katzenberg and said, 'You're going to replace me, right?' He said, 'No, Bob, never. Take my word for it, Bob. *Trust me.*'

"Then, my agent, who at that time handled Robert Wise, called up and said, 'Look, we've got an offer for Robert Wise to replace you on the picture.' Apparently, Paramount couldn't remember that we both had the same agent, so I called Jeff again and said, 'Look, are you going to replace me?' He said, 'Absolutely not! Never! You're absolutely staying with the project.' I pointed out that Robert Wise and I had the same agent, so he said, 'If *Robert Wise* doesn't do it, then *you* are absolutely going to do it.' I laughed about that for a while. I knew it would happen sooner or later, but I was more angry about the way it happened. I could understand them wanting someone else when the budget escalated, but I wish they would have been nicer about it and said, 'Look, these are the facts of the situation.'"

He's quick to point out that any anger he felt wasn't directed at Gene Roddenberry.

"Gene would often say about the script, 'This isn't *Star Trek.*' One could argue that it may not be *Star Trek*, but it's good and at the same time you had to realize that on a personal level, he was wrapped up in it," Collins explains. "His whole way of defining himself was involved with the series and with this project. I don't think any of us ever felt very angry at him. We wanted to help him realize his ambition, and we wanted to make a good picture, too. Paramount was holding a gun to his head, saying that they were going to do it, and then they weren't going to do it. That tension, I think, flowed through all of us. But, I liked Roddenberry and I always felt sympathetic towards him and the project."

Robert Goodwin didn't fare much better. "When they went with Robert Wise as director," he says, "Gene and I were never really informed of what the steps of the deal were. It turns out that Robert Wise is used to producing and directing, so I was asked by Gene and the studio if I would stay on as associate producer. I didn't want to spend a minute of my life doing that. I was an associate producer 10 years earlier, and it was like taking a step backwards, especially facing two years of production. So, I left."

David Gautreaux was next to depart, explaining that Wise was instrumental in getting Nimoy to return as Mr. Spock. Reportedly, the director wanted to know what ingredient was missing from the mix, and when informed, he demanded that the situation be rectified. At the time, Nimoy had been involved in a lawsuit with Paramount concerning *Star Trek* merchandise. It was quickly settled.

When Nimoy was signed to the project, Gautreaux *requested* that his character, Xon, be dropped from the film.

"I was doing a play at the time," Gautreaux recalls, "trying not to think that I was going to be playing an alien for the rest of my life. Then, I spoke to Gene Roddenberry and said, 'What's the story? Did you see that Leonard Nimoy is coming back to play his character? What's going to happen to Xon?' He said, 'Oh, Xon is very much

a part of the family and you're very much a part of our family.' I responded, 'Gene, don't allow a character of this magnitude to simply carry Spock's suitcases on board the ship and then say, "I'll be in my quarters if anybody needs me." Give him what I've put into him and what you've put into him. If he's not going to be more a part of it and more noble than that, let's eliminate him.' And that's what we did."

In regards to Nimoy's return to the *Star Trek* fold, Robert Wise has stated, "I was not very familiar with the show when I started and Spock did not mean anything special to me. I knew there was a character named Spock, but the fact he wouldn't be in the film meant nothing to me at the time. But after my wife, her daughter and my son-in-law read the script, they said to me, 'It's impossible, you don't have Spock, you cannot do *Star Trek* without Spock!' And they were Trekkies, so I respected their opinions. I went back to the studio then and said, 'We need Spock, otherwise the whole thing won't

work.' At the time, Leonard Nimoy had other commitments and I don't think he really wanted to do it. In fact, there was only one Vulcan in the script, a young guy named Sonak or something. Anyway, Paramount and he must have finally reached an agreement on a figure because he asked to see the script. We sent it to him, warning him that his character was not in it but could be written in that way and this way. And that's how we got him back. I'm really the one who made it a condition."

The *Star Trek II* television series had perished before it had ever gotten a chance to truly live. In March 1978, one of the largest press conferences of all time was held to announce that production would soon commence on *Star Trek: The Motion Picture.* At last, the long and rocky road of attempting to revive *Star Trek* had finally come to an end.

What follows is a guide to the scripts and treatments for *Star Trek II,* of which only two have been updated and utilized as episodes of *The Next Generation.*

"IN THY IMAGE"
Written by Alan Dean Foster

In early August of 1977, science fiction author Alan Dean Foster submitted a treatment for what was designed to have been the two-hour premiere episode of the *Star Trek II* television series. That treatment opened with the Enterprise on a routine patrol and receiving a Starfleet communication detailing the appearance of an enormous metallic shape moving through space on a direct heading for Earth. Kirk is given the task of intercepting whatever it might be, and altering its course. Information provided includes the fact that the shape is 30 kilometers across and 70 in length, and that it emits a radiation that causes automatic monitors to go "crazy."

As the Enterprise approaches, Lt. Vulcan (known from this point on as Xon – as this is who the character would have been if this version of "In Thy Image" had gone to script) comes to the conclusion that this is no meteor, but rather some sort of vessel. They pull up close to it and "the general effect is some monstrous cathedral lying on its side. Against that gleaming leviathan, the Enterprise is a tiny shape."

The intruder attempts communication, and Uhura puts it on speaker. Apparently the vessel is the servant of the God known as N'sa (pronounced "en-sah"). Xon checks with the computer and finds that there is no reference to a god named N'sa. The metallic voice explains that it is on its way to Earth, the home world of its god. According to the treatment, "N'sa showed the chosen people, 'we of the Wan,' the existence and magnificence of the universe. In return, 'we of the Wan' wish to return this gift by clearing N'sa's world of the festering disease N'sa indicated was poisoning its surface."

The Commander (now referred to as Decker) is confused by this, and questions the other vessel. Suddenly the metallic voice refers to him, and the others, as infestations. Before anything else can happen, Kirk orders photon torpedoes to be fired, but the energy proves to be harmless. Failing at this, he orders the ship to escape at warp speed, but to no avail. The Enterprise is being held in a tractor beam of enormous strength.

Decker is trying to figure out why the Wan has not destroyed them even though it clearly has the power to do so. Kirk deduces that it only wants to kill the crew, but save the ship, probably as a means of informing them of the Federation and its capabilities. Feeling that the loss of this information would become too great a threat, Kirk orders Scotty to overload the Enterprise's engines on his command so that the vessel will self destruct before the information can be obtained. With no choice, he gives the order – but nothing happens! Incredibly, the computer has refused a direct order.

"I have been ordered," the computer relates, "not to allow self destruction because it would not be to the greater glory of the great god N'sa."

Shortly thereafter, probes of light appear on the Enterprise, examining various aspects of the ship and, quite obviously, exploring the vessel, and then transmitting the information back to the Wan. A battle ensues, with the probes eventually leaving the ship. At that moment, the computer begins to feed information to the Wan, and ignores override commands.

"They're hunting for a weakness," warns Decker.

As the bridge crew ponders the true essence of their opponents, elsewhere on the ship there are reports of a tiger, a pack of wolves, an army of ants, alligators, eagles and elephants and lions. A swarm of bees materializes on the bridge, but most of those are disposed of via phaser fire. Xon picks up one of the "dead" bees, and discovers that it is actually a mechanical device, as are all the creatures that suddenly appeared on board.

They attempt communication with the alien ship's crew, and are shocked to realize that the ship is actually a single machine life-form. Bearing this in mind, Xon comes to the conclusion that the Enterprise was not destroyed because Wan considers it a smaller version of itself, and the crew a disease known as organic life.

Kirk does his best to convince the Wan that they are all intelligent creatures, but it wants no part of this. The alien ship will continue on its path to Earth, and cleanse it of the parasitic units. The Wan explains that "they knew nothing of the universe beyond until one day the god N'sa came down to them. N'sa told them of the universe beyond and the world it came from. So this great vessel was built to return the body of N'sa to its home and to exterminate the organic life that enslaved N'sa's companions."

Then, Kirk, Xon, Decker and McCoy are transported aboard the alien spacecraft, and appear in a huge vaulted chamber. Robot reproductions of Sulu and another crewmember wheel a mobile cart into the room with a clear dome cover. They're shocked to learn that the great god N'sa is actually a Pioneer Ten space probe launched by NASA in 1973. Apparently the Wan accepted the probe as god, and misinterpreted the information within it.

Through pleading for man as a species, and a plan in which the Enterprise crew had constructed a robot version of Xon equipped with a photon bomb, the Wan admits defeat. The bomb, it points out, is not the reason, but rather the fact that the superiority of intelligent life has been proved. The real crewmembers are transported back aboard the Enterprise, where they settle into their normal positions, and continue their mission.

Out of curiosity, Decker asks the ship's computer whether man or machine is superior.

"Man is superior, naturally," the computer responds, much to Decker's relief.

"Don't be too sure of yourself, Commander," says McCoy. "We'll always have to keep one eye on our machines."

"What do you mean?" Decker asks. "You just heard it admit that we're its superiors."

"That's what it said," smiles McCoy, "but how do we know for sure that it isn't lying?"

With that said, the Enterprise warps into space.

* * *

Upon reading Foster's treatment, Gene Roddenberry issued a total of six pages of comments, noting that the "principle problem . . . is certainly not lack of imagination. Rather, I believe most of my comments will bear upon control and selective use of imagination . . . Most of our story problem seems to boil down to getting to know our alien characters better . . . it should then be much easier to build a tale which rises steadily in excitement and jeopardies (to the starship and to Earth) to a very exciting and satisfying climax."

Series producer Harold Livingston was quite pleased with the treatment, although he agreed with many of Roddenberry's criticisms. He wrote that he thought they had a "very, very workable story and, assuming the writer shares our enthusiasm, I do believe we'll come out with a very good script."

"When they were thinking of reviving Star Trek," Alan Dean Foster relates, "a number of writers were called in to submit treatments for hour long episodes. Roddenberry had gotten in touch with me because of the Star Trek Log series. He felt I was comfortable with the Star Trek

universe and familiar with the characters. So I submitted three story ideas. I can describe one of the other two, but I forget the third. One of them . . . Roddenberry gave me a page and a half outline for 'Robot's Return.' He thought that could be developed and wanted to see what I could do with it. So that was one of the three things I took home and developed into story ideas, which ran about five or six pages each. One of them, which I would still like to do, involved the Enterprise arriving at a planet which was the 1860s South, only the white folks were the slaves and the black folks were the ruling class.

"Anyway," he continues, "Roddenberry told me to develop the story for 'In Thy Image' into a full scale treatment. After my treatment was turned in based on Roddenberry's page, it was decided to open the series with a two hour movie for TV, which is fairly standard procedure when they can manage it. It was decided that of the treatments they had at hand, mine was the best suited to carry two hours. So I went home and developed a 37 page outline."

Foster went on to develop his treatment for "In Thy Image" into a two hour episode.

The revised treatment, dated August 12, 1977, differed primarily in the way it opened. After the destruction of the Klingon vessels, we move to Starfleet Headquarters, where Admiral Kirk is reviewing a tape which details information on the refitting of the Enterprise. Captain Adams, who is to command the ship, enters the room and suggests that the admiral join him for the final precommissioning tour. As they leave the room, they're called to an emergency meeting.

It seems that Starfleet has detected a large metallic object on a direct heading for Earth. Enterprise is assigned the task of deflecting the object, but Adams is concerned that the starship isn't quite ready. Unfortunately, the new equipment already installed makes her the only vessel capable of accomplishing this mission.

Adams requests that Kirk assume command of the vessel, as a "newly refitted cruiser he could handle, a shakedown cruise he could manage . . . but to handle both of those in conjunction with a crisis of this magnitude is something he's not prepared for." Finally, and after much reluctance, Kirk agrees.

Kirk is able to reunite his original core crew, with the exception of Spock, who is now president of the Vulcan Academy of Sciences. His replacement is Lt. Xon, 22 year old Vulcan science officer. Kirk, and many others, are concerned about his age, but are told by Starfleet that he is the most qualified.

Despite minor mishaps, Enterprise finally meets with the metallic object, discovering that it is actually a vessel of some sort (as described in the synopsis of the first draft).

The rest of the draft is pretty much like the original in terms of story structure, though most events are expanded upon. The primary exception is the reason the alien vessel decides to spare Earth and the crew. Kirk's demonstration of human creativity touches something in the alien, which is going to take "the word of this creativity thing back to Wan. New information that requires much study. Perhaps if machines have helped man to achieve such creations, one day man might help the Wan to do likewise. It's a relationship which can benefit both ways."

"TO ATTAIN THE ALL"
Written by Norman Spinrad

From the bridge of the Enterprise, the crew is studying a group of artificial looking planets in orbit around a star "like pearls on a string." Kirk is awed over a civilization that can move planets around as though they were billiard balls. Xon points out that there is no energy or life readings, and that the ruins are actually billions of years old. Suddenly they vanish from the sector of the galaxy they were in, and find themselves in what is described as a "chaotic rainbow maelstrom universe of swirling colors."

The bridge crew attempts to sort out the facts so that they can get their bearings. Uhura tries to communicate with Starfleet Command, but these efforts are fruitless. No transmissions will go out and none are received. Ship sensors are unable to determine their location. Scotty, in the meantime, is shocked to find that somehow the matter/antimatter nacelles are actually composed of a third state of matter. The result is that he can't tell if the warp drive is capable of functioning or not. They soon determine that the only thing functioning properly is the life support system. Everything else is in utter chaos.

A bald, blue skinned alien, who identifies himself as The Prince, suddenly appears on the bridge. He is the last of the First Ones, the ancient race discussed at the outset which had the ability to rearrange entire solar systems to suit their whim. Kirk is incredulous, demanding to know exactly what is going on. The Prince explains that he is responsible for their being here and that this area of space has been designed to teach the galaxy of the Lost Ones, if they can prove themselves worthy of "Attaining the All." Decker and Xon, as representatives of Earth and Vul-

can, are invited to come down to the planetoid so that they can attain the aforementioned knowledge. Kirk requests that the Enterprise be freed as a sign of good faith. Xon interjects that the alien is showing no signs of life. The Prince disagrees, explaining that he has moved beyond living as a mortal defines the word. Again the captain demands the freedom of his ship, but The Prince counters that the only way for the Enterprise to leave is for the knowledge of the Lost Ones to be imparted to them. If Kirk decides that his people are not destined to attain the all, then the starship will remain exactly where it is for all eternity. It's decided that there is no choice in the matter. Decker, Xon and The Prince are instantly gone.

Reappearing in the maze-like interior of the planetoid, The Prince tells the pair that they must maneuver their way through it and reach the primary computer banks where the knowledge is awaiting them. If they are able to do this, then it will prove their worthiness to obtain the prize which lies in waiting. With that, The Prince vanishes and they find themselves upside down on the "immaterial" ceiling. Decker begins to approach the situation logically, while Xon tries to study it through human intuition. As a result, they find themselves right-sideup. When The Prince asks if they have begun to learn, they find themselves nodding in the affirmative. In Enterprise sickbay, McCoy and Chapel have gotten into a heated argument over the prognosis of a patient. In the midst of their fight, The Prince appears before them, explaining that they should merge closer with each other. After a moment's time, McCoy begins saying things which sound a bit like what Chapel would say, and vice versa. The Prince seems quite pleased.

Cutting back and forth between the maze and the Enterprise, the treatment informs us that everybody seems to be switching personality traits to some degree. The only one

unaffected by all this is Kirk, and this is chalked up to the loneliness of command. As a result, he sees what is happening and realizes that he's got to move quickly to stop it before the results are disastrous.

Gambling, Kirk informs The Prince, wherever he may be, that if contact is not made with Decker and Xon, then he will destroy the Enterprise and all the people aboard her. In response The Prince states that Kirk has won, but communication must be made telepathically through the minds of Xon and Ilia. On the bridge she begins to speak in Xon's voice, which allows the Vulcan to speak to Kirk and hear through Ilia's ears. Xon tells Kirk that they are nearing their goal. In the background, Uhura mouths these words as well. It seems that she too has become a part of this psychic link-up. Kirk wants to speak to Decker, and the commander begins to speak through the Deltan's mouth. Using the father-son relationship between them, Kirk is partially successful in bringing Decker out of this euphoric state of being. At that moment, the Enterprise lurches and The Prince states that only a mental link-up between the captain and Scotty can save the vessel. This is done, and they're successful. Suddenly it seems as though the entire group is locked in the same link. Every time Kirk proposes a question, they all respond in unison. The captain continues in his attempt to keep Decker from falling completely under the influence of the mind-link.

In the maze, Xon, Decker and The Prince enter the central chamber of the planetoid. There they find "an eerily glowing globe about twice the size of a basketball on a plain pedestal" (sounds remarkably like Sargon in "Return to Tomorrow"). Xon places his hands against the globe, and it's suddenly apparent that he is undergoing an incredible experience. Decker seems to be feeling the same thing. The Prince appears on the bridge, and the entire crew turns to

Kirk and in unison explains that the All has been attained. A moment later the, truth comes forth, a line at a time from each of the bridge crew. They reveal that The Prince is only a holographic image generated from the globe, which explains why he has been able to appear in more than one place at the same time. The First Ones, which were mentioned earlier, gave up both their bodies and identities to become godlike minds – the All, which is based within the globe that Xon had made contact with. The real plan called for the Enterprise to be merged with the All, and then the All, having acquired physical bodies, would be able to go deep into space and merge with all intelligent beings in the galaxy. The Prince thinks this is fair, because although humanoid life will lose its individuality, it will gain immortality. Now it is Kirk's turn to attain the All, or he will die. The bridge crew approaches him menacingly. Kirk begins to appeal to Will Decker, trying to convince him that he should retain his humanity and not let the All do this.

Still in the maze, but having heard the captain's words, Decker struggles within himself. Finally he touches the globe and is filled with "unholy ecstasy." He removes his hands, still partially himself, and vanishes. He materializes in a corridor near Kirk and joins the others in pursuing him. Once more Kirk tries desperately to remind him of who and what he is. Decker struggles again, and finally manages to snap himself out of the mind-link.

They proceed to engineering where they get into a fight with Scotty. The stress of this battle snaps the chief engineer from the link as well. The trio fight their way to the transporter room, sealing the door behind them. Decker, believing he remembers the proper coordinates, suggests that if they beam the globe containing the All deep into space, then it will be helplessly out of contact with the planetoid, which is its source of power.

The crew breaks through the door and is moving in for the kill, when the globe and Xon are beamed aboard the ship. The Enterprise is abruptly back in its own space, and the crew swiftly returns to normal.

Some time later, back on the bridge, Kirk, Xon and Decker are debating over how they should dispose of the globe. Xon suggests that, logically, the globe should be dispersed into space, thus putting an absolute end to its power. Kirk disagrees. "Maybe we can teach the First Ones a lesson in something that they with all their knowledge haven't attained yet – mercy," he says.

Scotty is ordered to beam the globe, in one piece, towards the Andromeda galaxy. Considering that it will take billions of years for it to get there, Kirk hopes that it will provide the All with an opportunity to learn about mercy and humility.

*   *   *

There's a certain attraction in the crew attempting to attain the all ... a promise of greatness. The only problem with Norman Spinrad's tale is that it's too similar to "Return to Tomorrow," and it's a bit disconcerting to see the repetition of ideas. Still, one can assume that Spinrad would have done a highly creative job of developing this treatment into a full fledged teleplay that would branch off in different directions.

In a letter to Producer Harold Livingston dated July 29, 1977, Spinrad detailed his initial thoughts concerning "To Attain the All." In that version, Kirk and Xon discover an artificial planet and beam over to it, where they learn that in actuality it is a living computer. A search for ancient knowledge begins, with the Vulcan believing that this will give him the opportunity to eclipse his predecessor, Mr. Spock, in knowledge and wisdom (of course one must question how sympathetic the audience would be to a Vulcan driven by such human emotion).

According to this document, Kirk and Xon go through much the same motions that the others did in the full treatment, and they "overcome strange pitfalls which sometimes pit them against each other, pick up odd bits of new knowledge, develop telepathic powers, go through subtle personality changes and become more and more like the alien race itself, particularly the Vulcan." McCoy, via the communicator, continues to remind Kirk of his humanity, much as the captain did Decker in the treatment. Xon has fallen completely under the spell of the All, and Kirk is the only one who can keep him from bringing this alien presence aboard the ship. Kirk partially merges with the computer entity, while still managing to hold on to his own identity. Scotty beams them to safety and the planetoid, perhaps out of hopelessness, self destructs; its knowledge lost forever.

On August 4, 1977, Gene Roddenberry wrote a memo to Livingston which said, in part, "We could use any ideas (which) might make this story work. Spinrad is brilliant and he is onto the right thing." Negatively speaking, he noted that the production probably couldn't afford the maze as described. "Also," he wrote, "it is largely a two-man story with them interacting with a 'hidden power.' It is hardly action-adventure. The jeopardy is mostly intellectual."

The entire Star Trek II company was very excited by Spinrad's full treatment. Roddenberry in particular had positive feedback, suggesting that perhaps the alien power could sway the Enterprise crew over by offering to give the individual whatever it was that they desired most. This, he pointed out, was similar but different to the premise of the original Star Trek's first season episode, "The Naked Time." Unfortunately, this idea was never taken any further, as the series itself was to be dropped shortly thereafter.

"They were going to do a two

hour pilot," says Spinrad, recalling his involvement with *Star Trek II,* "and commissioned X number of scripts and Y number of treatments. 'To Attain the All' was a treatment that never went any further, and they went the movie route instead and threw out all the scripts and treatments. I don't remember where the idea came from, except that I've always been fascinated with the high mind concept, which I have dealt with in books. It would have made a great TV piece because it's all in the acting. They all take on each other's characteristics which is something really weird and strange that wouldn't be as interesting in a novel, but would as a film or play. Something oral. Something with acting."

"THE PRISONER"
Written by James Menzies

While on routine patrol, the Enterprise communication channels are infiltrated by a variety of voices which are completely unrecognizable. The bridge crew can make no sense of what they are saying. Decker has Uhura switch to emergency frequencies, but they too are filled with voices.

Kirk and Xon enter the bridge, with the Vulcan identifying the voices as coming from Earth. The captain has a vague memory of one of them and requests an individual playback of it. Uhura does so, and they hear the voice of Winston Churchill delivering his famous speech during the Battle of Britain. From there they hear the likes of Gandhi and Harry Truman. Then the voices stop and the image of Albert Einstein appears on the viewer. Everybody on the bridge recognizes him instantly. Kirk is addressed directly, with the scientist explaining that he is in desperate need of help.

According to Einstein, he and many other Earth scientists were kidnapped from their native world and kept alive on an alien planetoid through the past several centuries. After he explains that he and the others have been sustained by some sort of "storage battery," he goes on to define one of his basic laws in response to Kirk's "quiz." Xon is impressed by the response. The captain is told that the voice matches perfectly with the computer's record of Einstein. The coordinates for the planetoid are given, with the professor hoping that Kirk will help him out of this dilemma.

Kirk does not truly believe that he was speaking to Einstein, but he is understandably curious and has a course plotted for the planetoid. Upon arriving, the Enterprise begins to orbit with phasers armed. There is no communication from the surface and, fearing a trap, Kirk is about to order the starship to break away when Einstein again appears on the main viewer. He wants to have a committee of prisoners beamed aboard the ship, but Kirk insists, above the man's protests, that a landing party transport down to the surface.

The landing party takes its place on the platform and the transporter is put into operation. Nothing happens. Moments later Einstein, with Robert Goddard, Marie Curie, Buster Keaton, M. Planck and Karl Jansky, appear [Keaton is described as looking out of place with his "quaint 1920 knickers and pork pie hat"]. Kirk is angry and wants to know what Einstein did to the transporter. He apologizes and chalks it up to their over-anxiousness.

Using his tricorder, Xon scans the group and announces that they are not really life forms at all, but rather perfect illusions. The Enterprise is ordered out of orbit and the six figures disappear. Unfortunately something is holding the ship in orbit and it cannot break free no matter how much energy is exerted. When it becomes obvious that this attempt is futile, engines are stopped.

Einstein's image reappears on the bridge viewscreen. He informs Kirk that he feels responsible for the atomic era and wants to return to Earth so that he can atone for the holocausts that followed. His centuries of imprisonment have given him the knowledge of how he can make life on Earth a paradise again. However, all that is left of Einstein is his mind, and he needs the Enterprise and her crew to get back to Earth. Kirk refuses and the scientist uses his vast mental abilities to assault the entire crew with a variety of voices and information which ultimately proves overwhelming to their minds, causing them to pass into unconsciousness. When they recover some time later, they learn that this attack on their senses has caused no permanent damage.

Kirk beams down to the plane-

toid, and Einstein's voice welcomes him to Galleas-9. As the captain proceeds down an underground corridor he is informed that the voice took on the image of Einstein because he is such a recognizable personality from Earth history, and was not a threatening presence in any way. The voice gives itself the name Logos, and then explains that it has become obsessed with Earthmen after listening to billions of words that had come from the planet. It is his intention to assume the identity of all human life, beginning with Kirk and the crew of the Enterprise.

On the starship, Xon has been using the computer to analyze the situation, and he finds it odd that each of the personalities they've had "contact" with are from the early 1900s. What, he wonders, is the reason for this?

In true character form, Kirk tries to argue that what Logos plans to do would be a great crime against the human spirit. Most Earth history shows that man had spent a great deal of time trying to break the bonds of slavery and had finally achieved this goal. To take it away from them now would be the cruelest of acts. Logos laughs this off, pointing out that the entire planet constantly lives under the threat of nuclear annihilation, and they are a very savage race. Kirk explains that what Logos knows of Earth is now ancient history. The alien concurs to the extent that most of the transmissions he received came from radio and television broadcast waves. When the form of transmission was changed in the year 2,024, he lost contact. But this doesn't matter.

"It does matter!" screams Kirk. "Earthmen no longer war against each other. The Federation outlawed armed space conflicts ages ago."

Logos cannot believe that man could change his basic nature that much. Such a situation would mean that the world would be no fun at all. Kirk is suddenly thrust against an electromagnetic conductor and held as "programming" is initiated. According to Logos, millions of facts from the storage batteries will be fed into the captain's brain. Kirk tries to fight back this assault, but to no avail. A short while later Kirk opens communication with the Enterprise, and peacefully asks that they beam him back aboard. He appears in the transporter room and is greeted by Decker, Xon, McCoy and Scotty. He explains that everything has been straightened out and orders Decker to have a course laid in for Earth. With that said, he departs to his quarters.

Decker is convinced that this is not Captain Kirk, and states that he is assuming command of the Enterprise. McCoy insists on examining the captain, and "making damn sure before his friend's record is smeared with a certification of unfitness to command."

Bones and Decker proceed to the captain's quarters, where Kirk/Logos programs them instantly – thus making them part of the one. Upon returning to the bridge, Xon is surprised find that a course has been laid in and implemented to Earth. He contacts Kirk and requests that he speak to either the commander or the doctor. Kirk/Logos sidesteps this, ordering him to have the entire crew gather in the rec room. Communication is closed, and the Vulcan begins

a search for Decker and McCoy. He finds them in a corridor, and they strangely turn around and begin walking back to Kirk's cabin as though summoned telepathically.

Xon proceeds to Scott's quarters and requests that the temperature in the captain's cabin be reduced and freezing ozone filtered in. Having already detected that something was wrong, Scott follows through with this request. Moments later it actually begins to snow in Kirk's quarters. Kirk/ Logos, Decker and McCoy all slip into unconsciousness. Xon proceeds to the main computer room and tries to devise a way that Kirk's power can be controlled.

Back in the captain's cabin, Kirk/ Logos, via a supreme mental effort, manages to stand up and overcome the numbing cold. He slowly makes his way towards the cabin door. Hearing the sound of footsteps on the intercom, Xon gives the order for the temperature to be lowered even more. Scotty refuses to do this (and we're never told why). Then the solution comes to the Vulcan. Since Logos had lost contact with Earth back in 2,024, there are over 200 years worth of information that he knows nothing about. The Vulcan has the computer feed all the information in its banks through Kirk's intercom, and the vast amount of knowledge is so powerful that it short circuits

Logos' mind and he departs Kirk's body and the ship.

The next day, the affected group is recovering from their encounter as the Enterprise is back on its normal course. Meanwhile on Galleas-9, the storage batteries are humming again, and Logos makes plans to update his laser radio-telescope. His hopes are high that man may some day regress to a more primitive state. The crew of the Enterprise proved to him that there's always hope.

*   *   *

With all due respect to writer James Menzies, "The Prisoner" would not have made a very effective episode of *Star Trek II*. First of all, it lacks the necessary dramatic elements to elevate the story from typical science fiction television fare. Secondly, the plot seems an amalgamation of the original series episodes "Return to Tomorrow" and "The Savage Curtain." The former gave us Sargon and his followers who wished to use the bodies of Enterprise crewmembers as hosts until they were able to create android bodies to house their highly developed brains. The latter began with the image of Abraham Lincoln appearing on the main viewing screen and requesting that Kirk come to a mysterious planet to help him. This too turned out to be a trap to test the basic nature of man.

"LORD BOBBY"
Written by Shimon Wincelberg

The Enterprise is en route to deliver live vaccines to the dying colony on Hathor-17, when it detects a derelict vessel called the Niobe. Radio signals are detected, but they simply cannot stop. There isn't time.

At that moment, both Sulu and Ilia note that something strange is happening. It seems that a tractor beam of some sort is being emitted from the other vessel and it is acting as a kind of "grappling hook," which, as a result, is creating a drag that causes the starship to slow down. Deflectors are useless. Uhura attempts communication, but there is no sensible response. The signals, which are described as "incoherent," are decoded, and all signs seem to point to the fact that it is actually a 19th Century folksong. Just then, the Enterprise comes to a complete halt. There's no choice but to send a boarding party over to investigate. Things go from bad to worse when they realize that the Niobe's tractor beam is actually feeding off the starship's engines, which are threatening to overheat.

Kirk has the computer give him a history of the smaller vessel, and he learns that the Niobe was a prototype sent out from Earth 20 years earlier, and that it has been equipped with a doomsday device to prevent its information from falling into the wrong hands. It had only been a short matter of time after its initial launch when it encountered, and was damaged by, a Klingon cruiser. The captain's dilemma is that the ship cannot be destroyed for fear of unleashing its awesome destructive power, but they must somehow find out what is controlling it.

Decker is in the transporter room, beaming over with the boarding party. He's horrified to discover that only Jennifer York, to whom he's been recently engaged, is transporting. Taking a dangerous risk, he jumps into the beam and shares her platform. They materialize on the Niobe. Decker attempts to contact the Enterprise, but is unable to because of a force field. Seeing no alternatives, they begin to make their way through the ship. En route they encounter "a number of nasty little shocks or tricks," and it rapidly becomes apparent that they are beginning to fall under a hypnotic spell of some kind which is leading them towards the bridge of the ship.

Once there, they are introduced to Lord Bobby of Yorkshire, who claims responsibility for all that they have been through. This person is dressed in Edwardian style, and claims that he is lonely for someone like Jennifer, whose voice he heard from the Enterprise bridge. He deems her a kindred spirit. Outraged, Decker explains that they were distracted from a mission which could literally mean life or death to a colony of people.

Realizing that his reasoning may not be strong enough for the humans, Lord Bobby utilizes his hypnotic abilities to convince them that he is actually suffering from a tropical fever, and that he desperately requires the attention of a physician. Decker asks him about the doomsday device, and is told that Lord Bobby had stowed away on the Niobe and stepped out into the open after a time to find that he was the only one on board. Apparently the crew had jettisoned the device, so any fears are groundless.

Within moments, Decker can sense the growing bond between Jennifer and Lord Bobby. According to the treatment we "also begin to note a subtle evasiveness about Lord Bobby, as well as a tendency not to let you get too close to him." Decker suddenly finds that he can contact Kirk, and is given permission to beam Lord Bobby on board the Enterprise so that the man can receive medical attention. For reasons that aren't explained in any detail, Bobby seems to lose his hypnotic hold for just an instant, and Decker sees him as a "clammy humanoid slug," while Jennifer doesn't. Full power is exuded again, and the monstrous image is gone.

Kirk accompanies Lord Bobby to sickbay and begins questioning him. In the meantime, the Enterprise has been able to break free of the tractor beam and is moving straight ahead. Ilia is shocked to find that the Niobe actually seems to be following them, and persists even after Sulu implements evasive maneuvers. Back in sickbay, Kirk, now under the alien's hypnotic abilities, accepts his strange story and "sympathizes" with Bobby's desire to want to return to Yorkshire.

Xon has been attempting to figure out exactly how the Niobe is following them when there is no one on board to pilot her. He develops several theories and proceeds to sickbay so that he may inform Kirk. Arriving, the Vulcan sees Lord Bobby for what he really is, and gets the captain out of the room so that he can explain that he's been under some strange form of alien hypnosis, to which only Xon seems to be immune [for which we're never told the reason].

Recognizing his own limitations in this particular situation, Kirk asks Xon to take charge of Lord Bobby. The Vulcan's primary concern is to stop the Niobe from tagging behind them. The alien proclaims that he has nothing to do with the other ship, while at the same time realizing that somehow Xon is immune to his power. To regain the upper hand, he uses his telepathic abilities to have the Niobe re-engage its tractor beam, thus stopping the Enterprise once again.

Ilia turns out to be immune to Bobby's hypnosis as well, so it is she and the Vulcan who realize that he is obviously seeking something. Logically, the longer the Enterprise is forced to remain immobile, the worse the situation with the colonists will get and the more likely it will be that the Enterprise will bring the alien to Yorkshire.

Kirk comes up with the idea of using Jennifer to persuade Lord Bobby to release the Enterprise. Naturally Decker isn't too pleased with this, but he follows orders. Jennifer approaches Bobby, and the two engage in a conversation where it's established that insofar as he can possibly be human, he is in love with her. Opening up his heart to her, he explains that he spent his childhood on "a planet colonized by Earth people from the Brittanic Commonwealth, whose 'superiority' and 'style' he had always admired." He had stowed away on the Niobe in the hope that he would someday be brought to the planet Earth.

The author explains that despite the fact he has been manipulating the crew, this exchange of dialogue would create sympathy for Lord Bobby for the simple reason that he is merely attempting to fulfill a dream. Essentially he wants to be human.

Jennifer tries to explain, despite his lack of understanding, how important it is for them to follow through with their mission. Ilia is disgusted by the fact that the human woman is unable to see through the hypnosis, and still remains somewhat smitten by the alien. Meanwhile, the situation on Hathor-17 is worse. Kirk threatens to destroy the Niobe if the Enterprise isn't freed. Lord Bobby merely laughs in response, stating matter of factly that the Enterprise would be destroyed as well. Kirk makes another attempt to board the smaller craft to disengage the tractor beam. Decker's landing party is unable to beam away.

The commander suggests that they use a shuttlecraft which he feels might be able to bypass the force field (why he would think this is never explained). Kirk agrees with this, but wants an unmanned craft to launch

first for safety reasons. The shuttle takes off, approaches the Niobe and is destroyed. Lord Bobby laughs this off, but it's obvious that he's grown somewhat weaker.

In a confrontation in the briefing room, Lord Bobby suggests that the Enterprise travel backwards in time, drop him and Jennifer off in 19th Century Victorian England and then proceed back to their mission, which will actually *gain* them time.

"Out of the question," responds Kirk. "It is against standing orders to tamper with Earth's past history, particularly by introducing an alien life form."

Angry, Lord Bobby uses his powers to make everyone, with the exception of Xon and Ilia, feel as though their blood is freezing. Perhaps this will convince them. When they're on the verge of death, he releases them and imposes a 15 minute deadline for a decision to be made. As the alien departs the room, McCoy points out that it seems that he desperately needs to restore his powers.

"Maybe," suggests McCoy, "if we can somehow destroy his dream simply by letting it come up against the jagged edges of reality . . . "

This makes sense to Kirk. Xon and Scotty will continue to work on a way to escape from the Niobe, while Jennifer will continue to attempt to make him see their side of the situation. She takes him to the rec room, where holographic images reveal what England looks like in this current time period. Studying them on a viewscreen, Decker is concerned about her feelings for the alien. Will she soon put her feelings above her loyalty to the ship?

All attempts at disarming the Niobe's hold on the Enterprise meet with failure. At the same time, communiqués from Starfleet Command constantly remind Kirk of how serious the situation is on Hathor-17. It's Chekov who suggests that they might have to kill Lord Bobby. Kirk disagrees, pointing out that the alien was

probably smart enough to rig the doomsday device in such a way that only his telepathic abilities will keep it from detonating.

In the rec room, Lord Bobby watches the images that Jennifer has programmed into the "holovision," but this does not deter him in the least. "Nothing," he says, "could be nobler than to die for the preservation of such a way of life." Jennifer is somewhat distraught, but, strangely enough, finds herself drawn even closer to him.

Kirk and Decker burst into the room, with the captain claiming that he challenges Lord Bobby for Jennifer's love. He asks the woman if she's actually in love with a human being who calls himself Lord Bobby, or is it in reality an alien being who is making her believe that he's human? Jennifer doesn't care one way or the other. Kirk suggests that if what she says is true, that the alien reveal his true self. Lord Bobby looks at her pleadingly, quite aware of human standards of beauty, and reverts to his true self. Despite being trained to accept a variety of alien life forms, there is nonetheless the slightest trace of horror and disgust in her eyes. Lord Bobby resumes his human form, and there are "tears of bitterness in his eyes." The only reason he had not activated the doomsday device was because he did not wish to destroy this woman he had fallen in love with.

Suddenly he grows contemptuous of human hypocrisy, and he reassumes his real body. With death soon to come, he has no qualms at being himself. Jennifer steps forward and explains that if he'll spare the Enterprise, then she will go back to the Niobe and share his dreams of Yorkshire for all eternity. He is touched by this, but there is a certain level of suspicion in him as well. Knowing his sense of honor, she offers to marry him to prove that she means what she says. The rec room is transformed into a replica of a village church, "familiar to Lord Bobby from something he might have read in Trollope or Hardy or Thackeray." He agrees, but remains on his guard.

While this is going on, Xon and Scotty continue their attempts to find a way of protecting themselves from the doomsday device. Xon believes that by channeling all power, including gravity and recycled air, to the shields, they would be able to generate enough power to protect the Enterprise.

The wedding is taking place, and during the ceremony Kirk objects, explaining to Lord Bobby that there is no longer a threat to them. His options are to beam back over to the Niobe or watch the vessel be destroyed. The captain shows him Xon's computer projections, and the alien realizes that he has indeed lost. He's more devastated by the fact that he has lost all faith in the thing called human love. Jennifer says nothing, and this adds to his bitterness. He decides to beam back over to the Niobe. Everyone is shocked when Jennifer is determined to carry through with her commitment to Lord Bobby. She will go back to the Niobe with him, and do her best to provide him with love. Touched, he reverts to his human persona.

Decker's eyes fill with tears as Jennifer and Lord Bobby prepare to beam over to the other craft. Lord Bobby sees the look shared by the two humans and, in his own estimation of nobility, nudges her off the transporter platform and "returns to his sterile, untroubled world of pure illusion."

*   *   *

"Lord Bobby" has some interesting ideas and is a touching tale of honor and sacrifice, dealing with the age-old theme of "beauty being only skin deep." Lord Bobby seems somewhat reminiscent of Trelene in "The Squire of Gothos" episode of the original series. One glaring problem with the story is the lack of explanation for Lord Bobby's waning power. Why is

this happening? And what will he do to replenish it?

Gene Roddenberry had a number of questions as well. For instance why would an alien get this obsession about 19th Century England? Even if he had survived on a Klingon vessel, how could this be the only Earth history on board? How can a vessel older than the Enterprise possibly manage to hold the starship? "These questions," wrote Roddenberry, "will have to be answered in the full outline before we can even consider putting it into script "

Some time later the basic concept of the story was altered, and it worked far more effectively. What follows is a brief recap: Starfleet sensors detect a possible intrusion of the Neutral Zone by a Romulan vessel. The Enterprise is ordered to investigate the situation. En route the starship encounters Lord Bobby's smaller craft. Uhura picks up singing, but all attempts at communication meet with failure.

A boarding party beams over to the derelict, and they immediately determine that this is an alien spacecraft, which is why it's so shocking to see Lord Bobby (who is described pretty much the same way he was in the step outline). He explains that he is actually Lord Robert Standish, the third Earl of Lancashire who was kidnapped from Earth by aliens at the beginning of the 20th Century. He had gotten involved in a space battle of some sort, and he was left with no way to get back to Earth. Out of a "matter of principle" he killed his captors, and has spent the rest of the time with his books of English literature.

Lord Bobby is overjoyed when he realizes that nearly the entire complement of crewmembers come from Earth, and he wants nothing more than for them to take him home. As before, he is instantly smitten by Jennifer, and he does his best to charm her. She's moved by his efforts.

Obviously this story is too much

to believe, if for no other reason than it would place Bobby's age at about 400. There's got to be another answer, and Xon hopes he will find it via a computer chip he discovers on the other ship. If it can be modified for the Enterprise's computers, perhaps it will shed some light on the situation. Once the boarding party has returned to the Enterprise and the investigation begins, they suddenly find themselves surrounded by five Romulan vessels, which launch an immediate attack. The warp drive is disabled.

The Romulan Commander states that the Enterprise had entered the Neutral Zone, which was in direct violation of the peace treaty between their two peoples. The Federation crew is to be considered prisoners of war and are ordered into Romulan territory "for questioning and detention." Due to the fact that the warp drive is nonfunctional, the Enterprise cannot resist the Romulan tractor beam which pulls them along. Kirk argues that they had been on a humanitarian rescue mission, which is the reason for their entering the Neutral Zone in the first place. The commander will hear nothing of this. He does not relish this newfound peace between the Federation and his people, and he feels that this violation is proof that the humans cannot be trusted. The only thing Kirk is able to do is convince the Romulans to tow-in Lord Bobby's ship as proof of his story.

Xon begins working on adapting Bobby's computer to that of the Enterprise, and Kirk orders Bobby to be examined by Doctor McCoy. While this is going on, the history section of the vessel is told to look back to the beginning of the 20th Century to see if there is any record of a Lord Robert Standish. Kirk also turns his attention back to the Romulans, feeling that they have fallen into a "carefully engineered trap."

The results of McCoy's medical exam come through, and it seems that Bobby is a normal 30 year old, but closer scrutiny reveals that his DNA most definitely is not human. History reports that there was a Robert Standish who mysteriously vanished in the year 1902. So there does seem to be some validity to his story.

Following this success, Xon states that he has managed to tap into the alien's computers. It turns out that Bobby had been a scientist on his native planet and was working on "a most complex and dangerous piece of weaponry when the strain of it had resulted in his race's equivalent of a nervous breakdown." His people had a method of dealing with insanity in which a mentally deficient person would be "dropped" into a society in which such behavior would be a natural, painless therapy for the afflicted until such time as they were cured. Bobby had been going through such a process, when he was withdrawn before being completely cured. The hopes of his people were that he could somehow save them from destruction. To save time in doing whatever it was that he was supposed to do (and, again, we're never told exactly what), his ship cut through Romulan territory and was attacked. Xon adds that Federation records do concur with the fact that Bobby's planet was destroyed.

Memory drugs are administered to the alien, and his mind begins to clear. According to the outline he is horrified on "two counts." First, because he is not really English and, second, he feels at least partially responsible for what had happened to his planet. His people were counting on him, and he failed. In the hopes of redeeming himself, he discusses with Xon the possibility of turning his ship into a bomb so powerful that it will be able to destroy all five Romulan vessels, thus allowing the Enterprise to escape. The timing, he adds, is critical, otherwise the Enterprise herself might be destroyed in the explosion.

Lord Bobby also states that in order to carry this plan through, he will have to revert to his true "repugnant" self so that he can operate the other ship, and he will have to pilot it until the moment of detonation, which means that he will probably be sacrificing himself. Nonetheless, honor demands it. Bobby and Xon beam over to the derelict.

Jennifer, who, as in the original draft, is smitten with Bobby, learns of his plan, and beams over via an auxiliary transporter. She searches him out and finds him in his true form. Horrified when he sees her, Bobby begins to make his way towards the chamber that will change him back into human form, but Xon restrains him, pointing out that there isn't enough time for such cosmetics. He needs to hold Jennifer, and throws the Vulcan to the side. Overcoming the initial shock, Jennifer says that she would rather hold him in his true form, and accept him as he really is. She still loves him no matter what he looks like. The nobility and honor of his heart is what attracted her to him in the first place.

Back on the Enterprise, Decker states that according to the records, there is no way for the derelict craft to have drifted into the Neutral Zone. In other words, somebody had to have deliberately placed it there. The squadron of Romulan ships had used it to bait a trap, and Decker thinks Kirk should confront the Romulan Commander with this fact. The captain concurs, but he wants to wait until repairs on the warp drive have been completed.

Some time later, the warp drive is ready and Lord Bobby's bomb is rigged. The plan calls for the Enterprise to go from sub-light to warp eight instantly, and before the Romulans can react they will be destroyed by the explosion.

Kirk finally confronts the Romulan Commander with the realization that this whole thing had been a trap. The Commander congratulates him, but points out that he'll never live to tell anyone about it. The Romulan vessels move in for the kill, but Enterprise warps away and Bobby's device explodes, destroying everyone there. Kirk orders a computer log of these events to be dispatched to the high command of the Romulans so the reality of the situation will be made clear.

* * *

The second version of "Lord Bobby" works a lot better than the original, answering many of the questions posed by Gene Roddenberry and others. This time everything seems much more logical, and Bobby actually comes across as heroic rather than a scoundrel. In addition, his sense of honor remains intact. The Romulans would no doubt have added an element of suspense if this outline had gone to script, and the episode would have given this highly neglected race an opportunity to strut their stuff.

"DEVIL'S DUE"
Written by William Lansford

On the bridge of the Enterprise, Commander Uhura picks up strange signals, which she and Xon determine to be coming from some form of intelligent life. Managing to lock on to the coordinates, the Vulcan states that it comes from a solar system which should not exist at all. The signals grow stronger and more urgent. Kirk decides to investigate.

Arriving at the proper area of space, they discover that the signals are coming from an Earth-like planet. A landing party consisting of Kirk, Xon, McCoy, Sulu, Ilia and Chekov beam down to the surface.

They appear, phasers held ready, searching for trouble. The people who eventually approach them are described as "shy and delicate, as graceful and beautiful as their surroundings. For the surface of this planet is beautiful." There is obviously no sign of hostility in any of them. They greet the Enterprise crewmembers by taking their hands, placing them on their foreheads and saying, "May joy dwell in you." Their leader, Raytoz, greets Kirk, welcoming them to Neutera and stating that Zxolar has been awaiting their arrival for quite some time.

They proceed to the rather humble and natural looking palace of Zxolar, where they meet Zxolar-the Blessed himself. He's described as a "beautiful old man – gentle and wise. Apparently he has been ailing for quite a while, but today he seems his old self, now that the Enterprise has arrived. Kirk comments that they have created a world of incredible beauty here, and that it is something they should be proud of. Zxolar replies with sadness, stating that in 20 days the entire planet will be destroyed by a sheet of flame and they will all be killed. In explaining the situation, the elderly man states that just over a thousand years earlier this world had been

on the verge of death. Zxolar himself was a part of the six-member Assembly of the Wise Men, and he is over a thousand years old. Using telepathic abilities only certain members of their society have, he flashes images of those days on a wall for the Enterprise personnel to see for themselves what kind of situation the planet was in.

When all hope seemed lost for Neuterra, a being known as Komether appeared and offered them one thousand years of complete prosperity in exchange for their planet at the end of that time period. Komether's plan was to dominate the world in ten centuries, destroying all life there and beginning anew. During that time, the natives of the planet were to construct the means of transporting themselves to another world.

"A thousand cycles seemed like forever," Zxolar says sadly. "It seemed unnecessary to concern them. Rather, they would move ahead, rebuilding their world, restoring technology and preparing for their exodus into space . . . only that time never came. Given their world back, the people wouldn't accept the science of industries which had once destroyed their environment. Nature became their theme and way of life, and so the centuries passed happily.

"In time," he continues, "Komether and our pact seemed as unreal as a troubled dream to the awakened dreamer." The reality of the situation, however, was constantly brought home because of the ancient scroll which served as the contract between the planet and Komether. With the exception of a handful of people, no one knows of the situation, or that their lives will soon come to an end. The only hope is to get them off of this planet in time. The Enterprise, Zxolar feels, is the sole method of attaining this goal.

Kirk, emotionally torn, explains that the Enterprise is only equipped to carry a few extra passengers, and that it would take weeks for other Feder-

ation vessels to arrive due to the distance of this galaxy, and that it would take days for subspace radio to transmit their message. "Then we're doomed," says Zxolar softly, his voice laced with regret.

The captain suggests that maybe he should speak to Komether. Zxolar says that he will try, but that the other being is hard and unforgiving and that, as they have long suspected, he is in reality Daimon – The Dark One.

That night, Zxolar uses his mental abilities to attempt to contact Komether. It takes some time, but he finally does appear in the form of a voice. Kirk wants to know why he wants to destroy these people. Komether says that their existence, or lack thereof, means absolutely nothing to him. The facts of the situation are that they signed a contract with him, and he gave them time to find another home. They did not, and it is no fault of his and no concern.

"But it's *my* concern!" Kirk explodes. "Neuterra's under the protection of the Federation – and I represent that Federation here!"

When Kirk replies to Komether's question of whether or not the Federation has laws, he is told to read over the contract and then to enforce it. "There is nothing more to be said," and Komether is gone.

Back on the Enterprise, with the clock ticking, Xon points out that there is evidence which suggests that the natives of this planet are descended from those who came from Earth. The idea is that some of the inhabitants from the Lost City of Atlantis might have escaped into the stars. The Vulcan adds that they may "be romanticizing things a bit," but this is nonetheless an interesting theory. Meanwhile, McCoy tells Kirk that he's been informed Zxolar has taken a turn for the worse, and has apparently lost his will to live. The man is in a near catatonic state. He is transported aboard the Enterprise, where McCoy will do everything that he can.

The starship becomes the victim

of various acts of sabotage, and it rapidly becomes apparent that Komether is behind it. Kirk demands that he reveal himself, and the being does appear as a kaleidoscopic form. His voice is angry, demanding to know why the Earthman persists in annoying him. Xon suggests that the facts of the situation be put in front of a Federation judge and jury to determine the legality of the transaction between the being and the planet. Komether states that he recognizes no laws beyond his own, and Kirk suggests (as he does so well) his "own logic is not as solid as he would like them to believe. That maybe Komether's power and confidence are nothing but empty bombast." This works, and Komether, in his arrogance, accepts this, but with certain conditions. If Kirk wins, then Neuterra survives. If he loses, then he forfeits the lives of himself, his crew and his vessel. Encouraged by various crewmembers, the captain agrees to this although he eventually begins to question his wisdom in doing so.

The trial is to take place in the briefing room, and as they proceed there, Komether takes a humanoid form and joins them, his chilling smile revealing his confidence. The judge will be the Enterprise main computer, with twelve secondary computers as the jury. Komether points out that this is certainly an impartial jury. Kirk's biggest argument is that the contract was signed by the natives of Neuterra under duress and the most adverse conditions. Komether counters with the fact that he has completely lived up to his end of the bargain, granting them 1,000 years of perfect prosperity. Kirk "likens this to a desperate man selling his soul to the devil." Komether suppresses a smile. Zxolar, who is at the trial, suggests that Komether take him and spare the others and their planet. The evil one just laughs this off. Zxolar appears to be on the edge of collapse, and McCoy suggests they take a break. This is done.

In sickbay, Xon explains that his sensors indicated that as Zxolar grew weaker, Komether grew stronger . . . at least his aura did. The Vulcan adds that in his opinion, Komether is not real. "There is no substance as we know it," he says. "There's only amorphous energy where he stands." He admits that he's confused by this, as is Kirk.

"Zxolar once referred to Komether as 'Daimon-The Dark One.'"

"Really, Captain," replies Xon, "you don't believe the philosopher made a bargain with the Devil?"

"The question is, Mr. Xon, does Zxolar believe it?" Bearing this theory in mind, Kirk approaches the old man and asks him whether or not he actually prayed for the Dark One to come to his people. Zxolar merely moans that they have made a deal with evil, and now they are paying the price. While Kirk and the other man were talking, Ilia "felt" images in the elderly man's mind. Through sheer force of will, she manages to project the image into the minds of the others and what they see is Zxolar and five other philosophers sitting together praying, and an energy form beginning to take shape. Apparently Komether was formed via kinetic energy – out of the will of the philosophers.

The trial begins anew. Kirk goes over everything that had transpired between Komether and the people of Neuterra, for which the Dark One is grateful. The captain adds that the problem is that the inhabitants of that world were misled, because Komether had nothing whatsoever to do with their survival or prosperity. "Komether was a myth," Kirk practically laughs. "A fraud." Komether is no longer smiling.

The computer asks for proof of this statement, and Kirk calls Zxolar to the stand. To prove his point, sensors scan both Zxolar and Komether, determining that the latter has neither form nor identity, but is actually nothing but a mass of energy created by Zxolar and the other philosophers. Kirk eloquently argues his point, constantly reinforcing the fact that Komether was created out of the sub-consciousness of those people who prayed to him. "Komether had been created out of fear and despair and he *was* evil – the Dark Side of your own mind. Every man has a dark side!" (And Kirk should know). Finally Zxolar finds the strength within himself to denounce the Dark One forcefully, and Komether fades into nothingness. Neuterra and its people are safe.

* * *

"Devil's Due" would have made a fine episode, combining the best of *Forbidden Planet* with a healthy dose of *Perry Mason*. The story is intelligent (albeit not entirely original), and the characters right on the mark. If developed a bit more fully, odds are that the "courtroom" scenes would have exploded with energy, giving actor William Shatner the opportunity to excel as Kirk. Alas this was not to become a reality, although the story was rewritten as an episode of *Star Trek: The Next Generation*.

Jon Povill was the *Star Trek II* story editor who had gotten even more involved with the show while Harold Livingston was writing the initial two hour episode. He wrote a memo to Gene Roddenberry in which he expressed his satisfaction with this story, with a few suggestions to make it better: "The character of Zxolar should die in the process of exorcising Komether during the climax, which should be a big, exciting moment that forces him to expend his last ounce of strength in order to eradicate the 'devil.' This element will eliminate the anti-climax that results from having to redeposit him on the planet after the excitement of the trial is over.

"Also, Kirk's decision to risk the Enterprise in agreeing to the trial must be justified somewhat more strongly than it currently is. The situation must be adjusted slightly so that it leaves Kirk virtually no alternative but to go ahead and risk the ship due to a very clear and present danger to the Federation if he does not. If these changes are effected, we feel that we've got the makings of a very nice episode in this one."

"PRACTICE IN WAKING"
Written by Richard Bach

The starship Enterprise approaches an antiquated space vessel. On the bridge, Scott wears a grin which betrays his delight. The other ship, one can only assume, is nothing less than a dream come true for the chief engineer; an opportunity to look into the past.

Looking up from his scanner, Xon identifies the vessel as Project Long Chance, which was launched from Earth in the year 2,004 and was the final such launching before the discovery of the warp drive. Ship's complement totaled about 40, all placed on a 10 year cycle of suspended animation. The vessel is undamaged and sensors detect one life form. Kirk has Uhura engage her console and attempt communication, but there is no response.

A boarding party consisting of Decker, Scotty and Sulu beam over to the Long Chance. They proceed down a corridor, which is lined with sleeper "caskets," and arrive at that of Chief Engineer Deborah MacClintock. Her monitor reveals that she has slept, awakened and slept again for nearly 300 years. The others register a considerably lower amount of reawakening.

While Decker contacts Kirk to have him link the Enterprise computer with that of the Long Chance, Scott accidentally brushes his hand against a control panel, and the words "Ready" and then "Theta Equalizer" flash on a monitor. A low humming is emitted, and the three men collapse to the deck without struggle. When they awaken, they find themselves in 16th Century Scotland, dressed accordingly, and without any memories whatsoever of the Enterprise and their proper place in time.

A troop of the Earl's soldiers pursue and capture a "powerful" witch. The three men from the Enterprise are angered by this attack on what appears to be a defenseless woman, and they too move in. They manage to chase the soldiers off, and take a strong look at the witch. It is obviously Deborah MacClintock.

The unconscious bodies of Decker, Scotty and Sulu have been brought back to the Enterprise. Kirk and McCoy are at a loss as to what has happened to them. "There's nothing to go on," sighs the doctor. "We stopped researching suspended animation 200 years ago with the advent of the warp drive. All I can say is that whatever happened was not chemically induced, and there's . . ."

Kirk grows angry at this. "I don't want chemicals, Bones. I want these men back now!"

McCoy explains that it is rapidly becoming a question of whether or not he can bring them back at all. Their life signs are growing weaker, and within 12 hours it's likely that they will be dead.

Meanwhile, MacClintock thanks the Enterprise men for saving her, but explains that it would probably be best if they went into hiding as "witch fever" is burning brightly. Scotty asks her if she is indeed a witch, to which she replies that she believes that it's true. "I get to dreaming," she says, "and odd things do happen." The men introduce themselves, but can't remember where they're from, although Decker does recall that there is something they're supposed to do . . . but what? They begin a walk to safety, barely avoiding a troop of 10 soldiers.

Enterprise: Xon explains that the sleep affecting the three men has been induced through sonic method and that it is being maintained at a deep theta level. He suggests that, logically, there would be a sonic device which could be utilized to awaken them. Kirk wonders if waking MacClintock would have any affect. The Vulcan doesn't think so, pointing out that in all probability she would die for the simple reason that at this time her body functions are operating at a level just removed from death. Tampering with the Long Chance's computer could conceivably kill her. Uhura has a data link patched in to the Long Chance's computer, and learns that the other woman is asleep and dreaming.

"The boarding crew," Kirk muses. "Are they dreaming?"

The three crewmembers of the Enterprise and the woman enter a tavern. The men obviously look quite tired. They sit down, and MacClintock explains that she believes she's sleeping somewhere and that this entire lifetime has been dreamt by her. In an effort to explain what she's talking about, she causes a bottle to rise a few inches and then settle on the table top again. When it explodes, she sheepishly admits that she doesn't have complete control yet.

All hell suddenly breaks loose as somebody has witnessed this demonstration and screams out that she is a witch. Another fight ensues, but it's obvious that the men's energy levels are decreasing along with their lifesigns on board the Enterprise. While Sulu proves that he could still fight them off, he nonetheless throws his sword over his shoulder and the four of them allow themselves to be arrested.

McCoy is growing more frustrated by the minute. Nothing he does seems to have any effect. "Modern medicine can raise the dead," notes Xon, "but not the sleeping." Time, the doctor sadly acknowledges, is rapidly running out.

The four prisoners are taken to the Earl's castle and, still bound, thrown into a stone and iron cell. Scotty discovers a knife in his boot, which Decker attempts to reach. MacClintock seems to be in some kind of a trance, which she comes out of a moment later to inform them that their bonds will now be loose. Within seconds they're free, and the cell door vanishes. She chalks it all up to her dreaming ability, and Scotty asks who she is and where she's from. "A ship," she says tentatively. "A ship in the stars . . . I'm watching us dreaming . . . this is not my home, this place. Scotty, this is not real. I've dreamed the whole lifetime. I'm so close to waking up . . ." They begin to make their way to freedom when MacClintock starts to disappear.

On board the Long Chance, the words "Theta Boost" appear over her casket, and her eyes begin to flutter. It appears as though she will awaken, but the need of the three men reels her back into the dream.

Making their way through the castle, they are once again surrounded by soldiers and this time offer no resistance whatsoever. The Earl approaches and explains that his people are absolutely terrified of witches and that he himself is rather uncomfortable at the thought of them. While there have often been accusations of witchcraft in the past, this is the first time that they've had firsthand evidence. As a result, the four will be burned to death . . . beginning with MacClintock.

With no alternative, Xon attempts the Vulcan mind meld with Decker and begins to describe the images that he sees, including the four of them tied to stakes, and the preparations being made to destroy them.

Before being gagged, Scotty mentions the words "long chance," and this triggers a whole stream of memories in the woman's mind. She disappears completely from ancient Scotland. The crowd is horrified. Guards approach and cut Decker's bonds, only to bring him to the stage where MacClintock was a moment before.

MacClintock awakens in her casket, and departs from it. She slowly makes her way down the corridor. Enterprise scanners detect that she is moving around and the order is given for her to be beamed aboard. She is brought to sickbay, where Xon is still engaged in the mind meld. "Sulu and Scott remain bound," he says in Deck-

er's voice. "I am being tied now, wrists behind the stake."

Realizing what is going on, MacClintock explains that the only way to awaken him is to make him conscious of the one thing he wants most in his life. Kirk has Xon place the image of the Enterprise bridge in Decker's mind.

Decker sees the vision and is suddenly unaffected by the flames which reach up to ensnare him. His bonds are gone and he walks over to Sulu, explaining that he is chief guidance control officer of the ship. The helmsman remembers, smiles and vanishes. Decker proceeds to Scotty, reminding him of the mechanical makeup of the Enterprise and the chief engineer vanishes as well. In a seemingly serene state of mind, Decker closes his eyes and all of ancient Scotland vanishes.

On the bridge of the Enterprise, Scotty and MacClintock are discussing various technical items. She explains that with the amount of time she has spent dreaming, she can't help but know that even this world and the Enterprise, with all her engineering and all her adventure, is still nothing more than a dream.

"And there comes a time when we must wake, even from lovely dreams," she says poetically, "but I'm remembering the day that I chose this lifetime, to be born to launch on a ship into the stars and meet a dear friend 300 years in my future . . . We don't have to die to wake, but even dyin' canna separate people who are friends." And with that she shimmers out of existence.

Scotty apparently has no reaction to this and Kirk, feeling rather confused, points out that she's gone. The Scotsman acknowledges this, pointing out that they'll meet again. But, he adds, if the Enterprise is only a dream then he'll only meet her this one time. "And I'll not want to be waking early," he smiles.

* * *

"Practice in Waking" would have made a beautiful episode of *Star Trek II*, providing a poetically dramatic

story with the opportunity for some of the background characters to get time in the spotlight. The idea of our very existence being little more than a dream is certainly an intriguing one, and it's a theme that was explored in an episode of *The Twilight Zone* in which a man, sentenced to death, tries to convince the world that if he dies, then they all will as well because the entire world is merely a part of his dream.

Richard Bach, whose varied literary efforts include *Jonathan Livingston Seagull*, proves himself to be a true fan of *Star Trek*, and one can only wish that he had had an opportunity to flesh this treatment out to teleplay form. It's refreshing to know that such a talent was being considered as a scriptwriter for the series, and it only makes one regret the transformation of *Star Trek II* into a feature film even more.

Bach submitted another treatment to the series, and in a memo dated August 29, 1977, producer Harold Livingston detailed his enthusiasm for the author and his efforts for the show.

"Richard Bach is a *Star Trek* fan," wrote Livingston. "He has submitted two stories, both of which were so eminently desirable that we purchased them. One story is a story of a society whose people are, for the most part, repressed and annually release their emotions by viewing their starships in combat with other starships. It is a very entertaining and provocative story and Bach has submitted a five page outline. Almost simultaneously, Art Lewis, a very accomplished writer, came in with a similar idea. It was decided to graft both of these stories and assign Lewis to develop the story and teleplay . . . At the same time, Bach's second story is what we consider a truly representative *Star Trek* vehicle, about a kind of dream world where our crewmembers become actively and dangerously involved in the dreams of a lady who had been in suspended animation for 200 years, kept alive throughout those 200 years with periodic dreams."

"A WAR TO END WARS"
Written by Richard Bach

The Enterprise arrives at the planet Shadir, a world the Federation has not contacted in over a century. Kirk is in the midst of studying the history of the planet's civilization, and the computer tape reveals that at the time of final contact, the Shadirians had just concluded their industrial revolution. The secret of their success is attributed to the fact that the race is more competitive than any other in the galaxy, and it's a dominant characteristic of the society.

At the time this tape was recorded, hundreds of cities were being constructed on the planet's surface. It had rapidly become a world of great beauty and splendor, and the threat of self destruction was relatively minor.

Spock [This is interesting. Could this treatment have been written before Leonard Nimoy announced he would not return as the Vulcan? By all rights, this character should have been referred to as Xon] concludes his scans of the planet, and raises his head as the tape comes to an end. The concluding statement explains that the Shadirians have never reached space, but at the rate they are going in terms of development it seems likely that it will only be a short matter of time before they do so.

Kirk is delighted at the prospect of making contact with a new civilization, but Spock dampens his spirits by informing him that the planet is "dead." There are no signs of communication, transportation or manufacturing systems in existence. The cities have been reduced to rubble, yet the atmosphere remains safe to humanoid life forms. Kirk is horrified by this information, and even more so when the Vulcan informs him that there is not a single life form on the planet's surface. The captain feels that he cannot accept this without seeing it for himself, so a landing party beams down. They materialize in the middle of what had once been a great city. Some buildings still stand, but the area holds a look of devastation.

Despite what sensors had indicated, there is a life form on Shadir, and that life form is a sniper who fires on Kirk and Spock with a machine-cannon. The attack misses them, but at the end of the street is a tank which levels its cannon barrel at them. A voice on a loudspeaker instructs them to drop all weapons. Reluctantly they do so. The tanks stops several feet in front of them, the hatch opens and a beautiful woman rises out of it, equipped with a machine-pistol.

"I've just made expenses," she smiles. "Step aboard, please, or die." Naturally, they comply.

They eventually make the discovery that they have been captured by an android, merely one "soldier" in a war between androids that has been raging on the planet's surface. It is a war in which, according to the treatment, "there are no refugees, no hospitals, no non-combatants. A war in which a soldier, mortally shot, can say, 'Oh darn it . . . ' with no particular rancor, and cease to function. A war in which there is no blood and no hate, no horror and no death."

In actuality, each android represents a real Shadirian, and the real Shadirians reside several miles beneath the planet's surface where, incredibly enough, there is a clear sky and a bright light. Apparently their underground world is more glorious than the surface had ever been. According to Bach's background for the civilization, it was the Shadirians' love for competition that gave them the "inspired" notion of creating a perpetual war, or, as the author puts it, "a continual Olympics, in which all who can afford the modest price of an android can participate." Their motto is "Keep the war on the surface," and that's exactly what they have done.

Moving back to the story itself, Kirk and Spock manage to convince the android that captured them that they are in fact living beings. This frightens the android, who realizes that she must get them to one of the underground elevators so that they can go down to the world where all living beings reside. This is easier said than done as they are confronted several times by the "soldiers." When it seems that the Enterprise crewmembers are about to be killed by a squadron of androids, their captor sacrifices herself so that they can make it to safety.

Once underground, Kirk is delighted to meet with the Shadirian who the android was modeled after. Her only disappointment comes from the fact that their experience on the surface had been a very expensive one. One android and one tank, to be exact.

Back on the Enterprise, Sulu is scanning the surface for a third time in an effort to locate the landing party. As before, the attempt is fruitless. All they are certain of is that Kirk and Spock were being attacked, and then disappeared. McCoy comes to the conclusion that the attackers must be androids, which is the reason there are no life form readings. The doctor and a security crew beam down to the surface and arrive at the location where the duo had been captured.

Deducing exactly what McCoy would do, Kirk has had an android sent to greet them and deliver the coordinates of the elevator. Acting on instinct, the doctor, who is startled by the approaching device, fires his phaser, damaging it beyond repair. Before its power dies out completely, McCoy hears Kirk's voice give coordinates.

McCoy figures out that these figures are for the transporter. In one hour, the transporter beams Kirk, Spock and the Shadirian girl aboard the Enterprise. The story ends with the implementation of diplomatic contact between the Federation and Shadir.

* * *

"A War to End Wars" probably would have been an interesting episode, and a variation of the circumstances surrounding the "A Taste of Armageddon" segment of the original series. In that show, the inhabitants of Eminiar VII were fighting a war with computers. When targeted zones were "struck," people living there would voluntarily walk into disintegrator chambers. The purpose of this was to continue their ongoing conflict with a neighboring planet, but preserve the technology of the two races. The Bach story, conversely, shows the society treating their war as a game. According to the treatment this system was actually looked upon favorably by Kirk, who is "convinced that it can apply in modified ways to several other planets and people."

"THE WAR TO END ALL WARS"
Written by
Arthur Bernard Lewis

The Enterprise achieves orbit around the planet Shadir, with Xon discovering the same circumstances on the planet's surface as Spock did in Richard Bach's "A War to End Wars." Scanners detect absolutely no sign of life.

Xon turns their attention to the viewing screen. There they see the remains of space crafts which look as though they have been through a battle. Sensors indicate that several of the ships still contain bodies. Uhura intercepts a distress signal, and puts it on viewer. Before them is a beautiful woman named Yra, who is pinned by debris. Dead bodies lie strewn on the ground around her. She requests that the Enterprise provide aid. Kirk has tractor beams locked onto her vessel and plans to beam over and free her. Xon asks that he exercise extreme caution. Scanners indicate that there is no sign of life. The distress signal, Kirk reasons, cannot be ignored. He turns the con over to Decker and departs for the transporter room. Kirk materializes in the other vessel and cuts Yra loose with his phaser. She is quick to explain that her ship was a casualty of the Shadirian War, a fact which depresses the captain because he had hoped that – based on what he had heard – the Shadirians had been able to bypass warfare.

Decker contacts the captain and informs him that a warship is closing in on them, which turns out to be the one that attacked Yra and her crew. Kirk gives the order for deflectors to be raised, but the Shadirian ship fires upon the Enterprise, resulting in severe damage. Yra informs him of the other ship's vulnerable spot and he, in turn, patches the information to the Enterprise. Both ships fire at the war vessel, causing it to explode. Kirk and Yra beam over to the Federation starship.

Returning to the bridge, Kirk studies a visual of the planet which seems "like a scene that resembles Berlin or London after World War II. All twisted steel and rubble." Then he is called down to sickbay, where McCoy informs him that Yra is a robot.

"I am not a robot," says Yra indignantly. "I'm an android." She adds that it's her duty to go back down to the planet's surface. Before Kirk can respond, he's summoned to the bridge. McCoy and Yra follow. The main viewscreen shows the image of a war vessel being readied for launch. Yra calculates that it will take off in two days, just hours before Scotty can finish implementing repairs to the Enterprise. The starship will most certainly be the primary target.

With Yra agreeing to help them, she, Kirk, Xon and McCoy beam down to the planet's surface, where they will be led to the control center. The street they appear on has obviously been mangled by war. They suddenly find themselves in the crossfire of two factions trying to kill each other. As they move to safety, McCoy uses his tricorder and discovers that all of the warriors are androids. Moments later, they find themselves captured and stripped of weapons, communicators and tricorders.

Plateous III, an elderly man of great dignity, approaches them. Xon quickly determines that he is an android who obviously commands the others. The people are ordered into a compound, while Yra is told to stay behind. Plateous III explains that her "debt" has been paid by helping restore the balance. It turns out that she is a spy who is angry that she was nearly destroyed. He tries to placate her by pointing out that the capture of the three aliens has put her ahead in credits. Yra wants to know if she will share in the credits for the 450 aliens on the Enterprise. He'll talk to her about it later. This angers her further

Kirk, McCoy and Xon, who are being held in a force field prison, are brought food by a living Shadirian named Zeylo. The captain wants to know if the androids have taken over the planet. Zeylo responds that the Shadirians live two kilometers beneath the surface of the planet and that there is a new passion for them which is known as "hand to hand." It's described as being the end product of space development. The Enterprise crewmembers, he continues, are rich prizes indeed and will soon become a part of the game.

Outside, Yra moves to the back entrance and laser melts the lock on the door. Making her way to the cell, she finds the Enterprise trio and explains that she had no idea they would be held as prisoners. She gets Kirk a weapon and departs at the sound of approaching guards. The captain is brought out to a compound where he is to engage in a battle to the death with an android fighter. Kirk is nearly killed, but he manages to destroy his opponent with the weapon given to him by Yra. Moving quickly, he enters the prison and destroys the force field device, thus freeing Xon, McCoy and the other prisoners.

The trio proceed down the road and are confronted by a Shadirian tank. Yra is the driver, and tells them to get in. They do so. As they drive along there is another attack in which Yra is seriously damaged. Xon manages to make repairs, but is quick to point out that they are probably temporary at best. As they head toward an entrance to the lower levels, Yra tells Kirk that the android war was created by Plateous II to provide a solution to the Shadirian's competitive nature, but now Plateous III has corrupted the system by allowing the taking of lives. Xon interrupts, stating that a changing of the guard is taking place at the entrance. Yra says that she is not allowed to travel below, so she provides a distraction while they do so.

Moving into a hotel-like living area, they see a wide variety of male and female Shadirians – all living. In one particular room they see a greatly pained Yra. Plateous III is standing over her, and the trio wonders if he is an android or alive. McCoy stays behind while Kirk and Xon continue.

Upon further exploration they find a room where Shadirians are sitting in plush chairs, staring at viewers with electrodes attached to their heads. According to the treatment, "The only sound is the click clack computer sound coming from each machine. The Shadirians do not speak, but their faces reflect joy, pain or horror – all the emotions of soldiers in war." A scream breaks out from one of them, medics carry the body out and a replacement takes the seat.

McCoy is attempting to aid Yra. Kirk and Xon return, and the four move off. Kirk wants to know why they have been allowed to move so freely and is told that "Plateous III is counting on the Android Controls to do the job for him." The idea is that Kirk will man the controls, but he is warned that the equipment will heighten every base emotion. The risk has to be taken. Xon will stay with Yra, because their primary concern remains the Shadirian warship. There is still a little time before their scheduled rendezvous with Decker.

Moving through the control room, Kirk and McCoy come across a Shadirian in a chair for "abort con-trol." Kirk dispatches him and slips into the chair. Electrodes attach themselves to his skull. He attempts to have the android on the warship abort its mission, but is unable to. He suddenly finds himself completely "caught up" in the war. McCoy is unable to free him. Shortly thereafter, Xon finds a way to shut the machine down and Kirk's limp body is removed from the chair. When he revives, Kirk tells them that not only couldn't he abort the mission, but all he wanted to do was kill – even the Enterprise officers!

When Decker and a landing party materialize, they are immediately under attack. An android speaking in Kirk's voice approaches, delivers some coordinates and is abruptly destroyed by enemy fire.

Xon, who is not likely to have any kind of an emotional buildup, takes Kirk's place in the chair and manages to abort the warship's mission. Guards enter the room, and haul out the now manacled Vulcan. Plateous III has the trio and Yra brought together. As a punishment for their treason, they will spend the rest of their lives working in a mine. At that moment, Decker and the fully armed landing party materialize. Kirk and the others (including Yra) are grabbed and beamed aboard the Enterprise.

Later, after full repairs have been implemented, Yra requests that she be transported down to another part of Shadir. There a reform group exists that is attempting to wrestle control from Plateous III, who has corrupted their whole culture of "peace through war."

"It's never worked," states Kirk solemnly. "Shadir's way has already failed. Plateous III has had to provide greater and greater thrills. Other planets have made it beyond the era of warfare. Maybe Shadir will make it too."

* * *

"The War to End All Wars" utilizes only the premise of androids fighting a war from Richard Bach's "A War to End Wars," but the story itself seems to be a direct opposite. In the original this system of "peace through war" was looked upon somewhat favorably as a method of working out a society's aggression. In this version, it's quite clear that the system has no redeeming values whatsoever. Once again man's basic nature corrupts what could be a positive means of dealing with its darker side. Actually, this is closer in spirit to *Star Trek*'s general-philosophy that any war, no matter its size or basic structure, is wrong, and cleaning it up in any manner or form doesn't make it any more desirable.

Arthur Bernard Lewis was going to develop this outline into a teleplay, but the assignment was withdrawn when the decision was made to produce *Star Trek: The Motion Picture* rather than a new television series.

"THE SAVAGE SYNDROME"
Written by Margaret Armen and Alf Harris

The Enterprise is in orbit around a lifeless planet. Sensors indicate a derelict vessel also in orbit, which Xon determines to be older than any known civilization in the sector.

Decker, McCoy and Ilia are given the task of taking a shuttlecraft to study the exterior of the cruiser before investigating her interior. Once inside the mysterious ship, they discover a humanoid skeleton with a "crudely improvised spear protruding from its rib cage."

Meanwhile, a metallic sphere is on the Enterprise viewing screen and drawing closer. Studying the object via computer scans, Xon announces that it seems to be a weapon of some kind. Before anyone can react, a pulsing light makes its way onto the bridge, enveloping the skull of each person. They collapse to the floor, and awaken moments later, snarling at each other like animals.

On the alien ship, Decker and company discover that the entire crew is dead, with McCoy theorizing that somehow they reverted to a primitive state of being and murdered each other. Studying computer logs, they see the metallic sphere affect the crew and realize that in some manner unknown to them, it removed all of their civilized instincts. Believing that these alien "mines" might still exist, Decker attempts to open communication with the Enterprise, but there's no response. They elect to return.

A now savage Kirk and Scotty fight over the command chair with a piece of pipe and wrench, respectively. "I sit here," snarls Kirk. "I am the leader!" Scotty and a fellow "green shirt" from engineering are thrust into the turbo lift and, therefore, trapped. Eyeing the balance of the bridge crew, it's obvious that Kirk has proven his point.

Moving seductively, Uhura sits by Kirk's feet, gently rubbing her cheek against his knee. Jealous, Rand sits near his other knee, and the two women eye each other with hatred. Smugly, Kirk places a hand on each of their shoulders.

Decker again tries communication, his voice coming through on the bridge speakers. The people are bewildered by this voice, seemingly coming from nowhere. "Who calls Kirk?" shouts the captain.

Uhura, followed by the others, shrieks at the sight of the shuttlecraft on the viewscreen. This stirs a dim memory in Kirk's mind.

Elsewhere on the Enterprise, crew members in blue battle with those in yellow, utilizing broken bottles, broken fixtures and whatever else is at hand.

The shuttlecraft comes to a stop in the docking bay. The now savage crew runs into hiding, alerting the trio to the fact that they've been affected. Decker wants to know if there's an antidote, but it's impossible for McCoy to discern until he's had the opportunity to study someone. Setting phasers on stun, they make their way to the turbo lift, having to use their weapons on fellow crewmembers who move in for the kill.

They eventually arrive at sickbay, enroute witnessing the results of a bloody massacre. McCoy secures the door, and announces that they'll be safe there for at least a little while. No sooner has he said this then Dr. Chapel leaps out of hiding and stabs Decker in the chest with a pair of medical scissors. Ilia stuns her, while a bloodied Decker collapses.

The bridge crew is busy fashioning primitive weapons out of chairs, consoles and other objects. Kirk pushes Rand away from him, demanding that she and the others find food. They begin searching every corner of the bridge, and Uhura lets out a gasp of surprise when she finds a panel that conceals stairs which descend into darkness. Kirk, equipped with his pipe-club, begins to climb down the stairs, followed slowly by the others. They eventually arrive at the recreation level, and make their way to the commissary, where other crewmembers are fighting over the remains of a meal. Kirk and his followers take over the area, driving the others out and begin feasting on their find.

In sickbay, a restrained Chapel is rendered unconscious by McCoy's hypo-gun. Decker's chest has been bandaged in medi-skin and he seems to be okay. He wants to know if the doctor has learned anything yet. "Chapel's brain scan shows that the intellectual lobes of her mind were immobilized by the emanations," explains McCoy, who is running tests to determine whether or not this state of mind can be reversed.

Ilia suggests they make their way to the bridge so that they can flood the ship with tranquilizer gas, thus stopping the crew from killing each other. Decker passes out at that moment, and Ilia, noting that a medical officer lacks jurisdiction, orders McCoy to stay with him while she makes an attempt to reach the bridge.

Scotty and his assistant, having escaped from the turbo lift, arrive on the recreation level. Eyeing them suspiciously, Kirk gives the order for them to be killed. His people begin to pursue the two men.

Ilia arrives on the deserted bridge and is surprised by the dismantled equipment. She contacts McCoy and alerts him to the fact that it will be impossible for her to flood the ship. His antidote is their only hope.

Kirk and his followers pursue Scotty and the others into engineering, and stop when they see other "greens." Scott tells them that he is their leader and he will get them food. A savage fight erupts between the two factions, in which Scott is knocked against a console, accidentally hitting a control panel. A moment later, the computer's voice echoes, "Antimatter energy converters are now on overload ... detonation in sixty one minutes." The savages are terrified by this sound which seems to surround them.

Ilia has activated the computer to feed information to the doctor, and is attempting to shut down the ship's generators when Kirk and the others arrive on the bridge and surround her. Kirk chases her into the turbo lift, and she orders it to go to the sixteenth level. Contact is made with sickbay to appraise Decker and McCoy of her situation. They'll meet her on sixteen as soon as they can. She has the lift return them to the bridge at emergency speed, and then, also at emergency speed, she has the lift go back up to the twenty second level. Repeating this action again and again, she manages to keep knocking Kirk to the ground with the force of the sudden lurching. Confused and furious, he slowly manages to gain a firm hand-hold.

Standing outside the turbo lift doors on the sixteenth level, McCoy, using his communicator, informs Ilia that he's ready. The doors open, and Kirk locks eyes with him.

"Sorry, Jim," says the doctor as he stuns his friend, secures Kirk within the turbo lift, and they go back to sickbay. Studying the computer screen, McCoy regretfully informs them that there is no cure possible. Decker disagrees.

"We snare one of those mines," he explains, "get into it, reverse the frequency of the radiation emanated from it and detonate it . . . The savage syndrome was caused by pulsed light and electromagnetic radiation on a specific frequency. The effect can be reversed by altering that frequency, and generating it from a similar power source."

Decker says that he will use the shuttlecraft in an attempt to get one of the mines. They enter the turbo lift, where Kirk is now feigning uncon-sciousness. Decker, McCoy and Ilia depart at their destination, while the captain gets the lift to move by saying, "Lift to bridge."

Xon sits in the command chair, with Rand and Uhura lounging at his feet. Kirk swaggers onto the bridge once again, announcing that he is the leader. A fight erupts between him and the Vulcan, and it's soon obvious that Xon's superior strength is giving him the upper hand. Kirk is knocked against a computer console, where he discovers the phaser that Ilia had left there previously. Working on instinct, he raises the weapon and fires it. Xon sinks to the floor and the rest of the bridge crew stares at Kirk in awe.

"Kirk will lead all tribes," he announces while leading them into the turbo lift.

Shortly thereafter, they arrive in engineering and engage in another confrontation with Scotty and his men. Kirk stuns Scotty and several others. McCoy and Ilia are witness to this and realize that the only solution is to make a tranquilizer bomb. The computer announces that detonation will take place in twenty seven minutes. Unable to build the tranquilizer bomb, McCoy and Ilia go back to engineering and hide until Kirk and the now united "greens" and "reds" depart the area. Discovering that the engine's overload cannot be corrected without manual aid, McCoy tells Decker to get the mine on board the Enterprise as quickly as possible, because they need to have Scott back to normal.

Scotty is suddenly behind McCoy, grabbing him viciously around the throat and taking his phaser as well as Ilia's, thus making him "the strongest." McCoy pleads with the chief engineer, trying to somehow convince him of the danger they're all in, but to no avail. Trying a different tact, Ilia utilizes her considerable Deltan charms to make him remember, but, just as they're beginning to have an effect, he pushes her away from him.

Five minutes left before detonation.

Due to his wound, Decker struggles to remain conscious. After an agonizing effort, he activates the mine and it flares with the same pulsating light as in the beginning. The light makes its way through the Enterprise, enveloping the head of each crewmember. A moment later, everyone is cured.

With 58 seconds left before detonation, Scotty realizes what's happening and runs to the computer console. Kirk and Xon enter the room, offering their assistance. With one second left, Scott manages to override the engines.

Later, on the bridge, Ilia and McCoy explain what had happened and why Decker is recuperating in sickbay. Scotty is shocked at his reported actions.

"Shame we can't remember anything," says Kirk.

"It is," replies Ilia huskily while running her fingers through his hair. "You were a magnificent savage."

Kirk suppresses a smile.

The starship Enterprise breaks orbit, leaving behind the lifeless planet.

* * *

"The Savage Syndrome" would have made an interesting *Star Trek II* episode. While lacking the philosophical edge of many of the finer shows, it did hold the promise of an exciting and fascinating adventure.

An interesting point of characterization is that of Kirk appointing himself leader, as though he would be destined for such a role no matter what kind of life he was born in to. Bearing this in mind, it's logical that he would be the first to grasp certain ideas.

From a production standpoint, this episode would have been quite important for the simple reason that it was primarily a ship-board story, and, therefore, more cost effective than the average episode. This had been a problem that occurred during the run of the original series, and one that has arisen again for *Star Trek: The Next Generation.*

In a memo dated September 2, 1977, Producer Bob Goodwin wrote ". . . in order to do an effective job on our stories that take place in settings other than the Enterprise, and still remain within our financial and production limitations, it is absolutely vital that we have an equal number of ship-board stories . . . If we don't have some good Enterprise stories in our back pockets, we could find ourselves with very serious production problems come December."

The memo specifically cited "The Savage Syndrome" as a perfect example. The first draft of the outline had Decker, McCoy and Ilia actually land the shuttlecraft on the surface of the planet, where they studied ancient ruins as well as "several other things that they encounter." Goodwin made the suggestion that the shuttle be investigating an object in space; this way it "would confine our story for the most part to the Enterprise." The second draft of the outline made this adjustment.

Incidentally, that first outline, dated September 28, 1977, holds some subtle, yet significant, differences which should have been left in the final script.

First of all, Kirk and his people manage to capture McCoy, Decker and Ilia. They attempt to stir the captain's memories, but the effort is fruitless. Attempting to "deal with primitives on their own level," McCoy magnifies the planet on the viewing screen, thus causing pandemonium to break out among the savages on the bridge. With this diversion, they escape into the turbo lift, but Kirk restrains Ilia (although the doctor and commander eventually rescue her).

An interesting scene took place in the recreation level, where McCoy threatens to bring the wrath of the gods upon the primitives. On cue, Decker activates the proper controls and "the walls become a crashing ocean, the air filled with the thunder of the waves and wind. An instant later the ocean becomes a World War II battlefield – shells bursting, cannon fire, and the deafening shrieks of the wounded." From there, the image becomes a raging fire, earthquakes, and so on. Once Decker, McCoy and Ilia depart, Kirk fumbles with the console and shuts the device off.

These illusionary walls were probably inspired by Ray Bradbury's "The Illustrated Man," while the scene itself was suggested by Producer Harold Livingston.

"Wouldn't it be more exciting and interesting if either Decker or McCoy – or both – used their brains to outwit the savages?" asked Livingston

in his notes regarding the story. "For example, they might use the viewing screens and other instruments to completely enthrall the Savages, perhaps even on the level of the old 'B' movies where the white explorer, knowing the moon was due to eclipse, filled the natives with awe and dread when he promised to make the sky dark and (as the eclipse occurred) did!" Livingston was right, and the scene would have played most effectively.

The conclusion of the story was also considerably different from the final script. Kirk is strangling McCoy, who manages to say, "Jim, for God's sakes, let me save the ship!"

Somehow these words have such an effect on Kirk that they snap him out of the Savage Syndrome, and he, rather than Scotty, stops the engines from over-loading. This, at least, was an understandable deletion from the story, as it wouldn't have made much sense and, in effect, meant that this primitive state of being would eventually wear off the crew without an antidote being needed.

The tag of the episode would have had Ilia expressing that it's frightening to realize how thin the veneer of civilization is.

"Yes," Kirk agreed. "Scratch the man, and the savage bleeds."

"THE CHILD"
Written by Jaron Summers and Jon Povill

A relief crew operates the bridge of the Enterprise. Xon sits in the command chair, and a look akin to boredom is evident on the faces of the humans there. Ensign Bernstein informs the Vulcan that there is a nebula of some kind on the main viewing screen. Junior Science Officer Park operates scanners and states that she's picking up several kinds of energy with radiation readings unlike any she has seen before.

A gaseous mass of energy appears before them and the Enterprise finds itself heading right towards it. Park interjects that readings indicate the radiation and electromagnetic levels are well within tolerance level. Xon has deflectors raised, and orders the Enterprise to be flown through the cloud at warp one, while surveying it for future study.

As the massive starship comes out the other side of the cloud, it is followed by a "large pulse" of white light which passes through the hull of the Enterprise. The light moves slowly down a corridor, passes through a wall, covers Uhura's sleeping body, and then moves on. Uhura shifts sensually in her bed, as though the light had brought with it an erotic touch. It proceeds to Chekov's and then Lt. Ilia's cabin. It's obvious that she is enjoying the touch of this strange entity. Then, according to the script, "it plunges inside her through her abdominal wall. Her body moves spasmodically, sexually; but she doesn't wake up." Ilia begins to glow as the light leaves her body and then, in turn, departs the starship to rejoin the cloud.

The next "morning" Lt. Ilia comes to sickbay just as McCoy is preparing for the day ahead of him. She is confused, instantly stating that she has not broken her vow of celibacy, and yet she has a memory of a pure white

and beautiful light. McCoy is confused, and asks that she try to make sense.

"I'm pregnant, Doctor," she announces.

McCoy's medical log states that it's only been three days since Ilia announced her pregnancy, and yet her child has gone through the 10 month gestation period common to Deltans. She is about to give birth, and he is understandably concerned about the nature of the child that she is carrying.

Returning to his patient, the doctor is surprised to find that she is actually trying to calm *him* down. Reassuring him that everything is going to be fine, Ilia states that "she" will be out in just a moment.

While McCoy goes to work, security officer Ling approaches them, a phaser in one hand and a medical tricorder in the other. The doctor is angered, stating that this unborn child has been identified as a female humanoid and poses absolutely no apparent threat to the Enterprise. Ling explains that he's merely following the orders of Captain Kirk. McCoy orders Ling out of there, and he reluctantly departs just as Doctor Chapel walks in. McCoy asks that she operate the intercom to the bridge. He hears Kirk's voice, and asks that Ilia have her child in peace. The captain points out that these are abnormal circumstances and all precautions must be taken. McCoy doesn't care what the circumstances are. He wants nothing to happen that might endanger the lives of Ilia or her child.

Signing off, Kirk glances around the bridge and takes note of half accusing stares – particularly from Decker. Feeling a need to defend his action, Kirk says that they don't know what it was that impregnated Ilia or why it was done. Decker points out that a newly born creature, human or not, is unlikely to pose a real threat to anyone. The captain wants to know if he can guarantee this.

"No sir," replies Decker with a shake of his head. "But for a child to be born with a phaser leveled at its head doesn't guarantee it either."

A nice touch.

Some time later, McCoy is holding a baby girl with a full set of hair. Kirk is looking at the child through the viewscreen and his expression reflects wonder, awe and concern.

When asked about a name for the baby, Ilia responds that she will call her Irska, which in Deltan translates to pure light. The woman seems to be glowing with love and affection for her child.

Back on the bridge, Uhura is curious if Ilia will be able to keep the child if it turns out to be normal. Kirk is doubtful that it is, for the simple reason that an immaculate conception followed by a three day gestation period can hardly be considered normal. What, then, will happen to Irska? Xon approaches the command chair and points out that there is no bond stronger than the one between a Deltan mother and her child. "In ancient times," he says, "protecting their offspring, Deltan women had been known to slay, barehanded, gnutabeasts five times their size."

(As a sidenote, not only does this dialogue give us a bit of insight concerning Deltans, but it once again establishes the fact that Xon considers himself something of a historian; possibly even more so than Mr. Spock. We would also see evidence of this in John Meredyth Lucas' "Kitumba." What's perhaps most interesting about this aspect of the character is that it's not even mentioned in the writer/director's guide for the series. One could see that the scripts were already beginning to add layers onto the characters, and this probably would have translated quite well from paper to celluloid. Anyway, we continue . . .)

Kirk is summoned to sickbay. While Ilia hugs and kisses her child, McCoy pulls him over to the side so that they can talk in private. The doctor explains that all tests indicate that Irska checks out human in every way and there are no Deltan characteristics at all. She even has hair on her head. What's really shocking is that his tests have shown that she is aging one year for every 24 hour period. Trying to figure out what to do, Kirk asks what the result would be if he was to separate Ilia and the child. McCoy thinks that such an action would be a drastic mistake for the simple reason that Ilia would stop at nothing to get her back. He's surprised that Kirk would even consider such a course of action. Naturally, the captain responds that he's considering the safety of the Enterprise and her crew. Once again, he wants to know why an alien life form had impregnated her without permission.

"It may be unusual," says McCoy, "but it's not altogether unique for a species to reproduce by depositing eggs in a host – without consent."

Kirk jumps on this, adding that in nearly every such situation the reproducing life form is of a parasitic nature. Attempting to ease his friend's concern, McCoy adds that he doesn't think the child will live until the end of the week. Her body has an abnormally high count of white blood cells. She's suffering from leukemia, and the normal antidotes to cancer seem to have no effect. Their conversation is interrupted by Uhura's voice, which informs them that there is an alien object approaching. Kirk tells her to put the ship on yellow alert and that he's on his way. Turning his attention back to the doctor, he wants to know if Ilia is aware of the situation. He hasn't told her yet, and is asked not to.

Later, in Ilia's quarters, she informs her daughter (who is now of a speaking age) that it is time for her to go back on duty. Irska wants to go with her, but the Deltan points out that it is important for the child to spend some time by herself because

it will give her the opportunity to begin to understand who she is to someday become. From there, Ilia goes to Kirk's quarters and requests that she be allowed to resume her station. The captain sidesteps the question by instead asking her about Irska. Ilia immediately grows defensive. He ponders the possible connection between her daughter and the cylinder in space. Ilia sees no connection. Nodding, Kirk gives her permission to return to the bridge.

Back on the bridge, Ilia relieves Chekov from the navigation station. The intruder alert system comes to life, and the Russian moves quickly to his station. Kirk steps out of the turbolift, and asks for a status report.

Xon explains that something is being beamed aboard the Enterprise from the alien cylinder, and that the object is one cubic centimeter of the radiation detected. With alarm in his voice, Chekov informs them that it "has beamed to the number ten filter in our atmospheric purification system." Kirk orders them to breakaway at warp six, which they do, but the cylinder follows them even after speed has been increased to warp eight. Nine point two fails to elude the object as well. The captain, realizing that all efforts are proving futile, orders engines stopped. Irska walks on the bridge and approaches Ilia, who strokes her hair lovingly. Glancing from mother and daughter to Kirk, Xon whispers that they have another problem. The radiation in the purification system is quite lethal. Unless it is counteracted in twelve hours, the entire crew will be dead.

Four hours later, Kirk tapes a captain's log which states that Doctors McCoy and Chapel have been unable to come up with a cure for the effects of the radiation, and the crew is already showing signs of poisoning.

Irska makes her way to engineering, where a very pained Mr. Scott actually seems happy to see her. In fact, he gives her a "home made" Deltan head band similar to the one

that Ilia wears. The difference is that this one will grow as the child does. Irska is very touched by this gesture of kindness, and puts it on.

Kirk is attempting to figure out why the cylinder would want to kill them slowly when it could obviously do it much quicker. Xon suggests that perhaps it is studying their reaction to the atmosphere. When Ilia enters the bridge, Kirk asks her if it's possible that this radiation has been used to trigger some kind of metamorphosis in Irska. Xon interjects that if this is a possibility, then McCoy should examine the child again. Ilia protests, but Kirk is firm in his agreement with the science officer.

Shortly thereafter, Ilia enters the captain's quarters and informs him that Irska has been brought to sickbay. The Deltan is obviously still very defensive about what is happening to her daughter. They get into a discussion about the situation when McCoy, equipped with a hypo, enters with Irska following. The child states that McCoy has taught her all about life and death, and the doctor adds that the white cells in her bloodstream had the cure that they were looking for. Everybody in the room appears relieved, except for Kirk.

The Enterprise is being penetrated by an energy beam from the cylinder. Kirk proceeds to the bridge. Once there, he is informed by Scotty that impulse engine servo units have been fused, and there is a leak in the number two cooling coil. Chekov informs Kirk that the radiation level in the access tube is higher than tolerance limit – seven with protection. Repairs are initiated, and Ilia is ordered to take Irska off the bridge.

Later, Uhura comes to Ilia's cabin and tries to explain to Irska that Captain Kirk is under a great strain, and when people are under such pressure they tend to say things that they don't really mean. Irska understands completely, and the love that emanates from her seems to touch Uhura.

Xon looks up from his bridge scanner and informs Kirk that he has tied into McCoy's computer medical profile of the child, and it is his estimation that Irska can survive the radiation being released from the impulse engine cooling core. There are most definitely some risks, but Xon believes they would be well worth taking. Decker points out that Ilia would never allow such a thing, so the Vulcan suggests that they not inform her of what they're doing. Decker is appalled at such a "cold blooded" thought.

"I believe the alien deliberately damaged us in an area that only Irska could enter," Xon gently points out, "just as the cure Doctor McCoy discovered could only come from her blood."

Kirk reluctantly has Ilia bring Irska back to the bridge. Once they arrive, Xon explains the situation. The Deltan truly wants no part of such an attempt, but Irska is adamant that she help in any way that she can because Mr. Scott is her friend, and he'll die if she does nothing. Xon gives her a welding torch and instructions, and they proceed to the access tube. The Vulcan pulls the now unconscious Scotty from the tube. Irska takes his place and immediately goes to work.

Xon explains that Irska will undoubtedly emerge from the tube with no ill effects from the radiation. He cautions that recent events suggest that another dilemma will formulate immediately after this one is abated.

"No life form in the entire galaxy can spoil good news faster than your average Vulcan," muses McCoy.

Xon requests permission to attempt a mind meld with Irska which may unlock some answers to what has been happening. Their attention turns to Irska as she emerges from the tube – completely unharmed. Xon induces the Vulcan technique, and experiences a variety of emotions. The final words he says are "Understand cryontha . . . End peril."

On the bridge, Uhura contacts Kirk and Xon, informing them that the alien cylinder is now being enveloped in an energy field. Chekov adds that this energy is breaking up the molecular structure of the Enterprise hull. Uhura is shocked upon realizing that the ship will actually turn to powder within 12 minutes. Kirk turns his attention back to Irska, asking her if she understands what the word peril means. She says that she does. When he asks about cryontha, she has no idea.

Within minutes, the ship's various systems begin to approach overload. There are nine minutes left before complete molecular breakdown. Kirk, who has now returned to the bridge, orders phasers fired at the cylinder. The beams lash out and strike the object. In response, Irska screams out in excruciating pain, and collapses to the floor. Xon says that besides the pain in Irska there is no damage to the cylinder. Despite the reaction on the child's part, Kirk orders another phaser blast. The results are exactly the same. Security is ordered to bring Ilia and Irska to their quarters. Before the Deltan can be escorted off the bridge, she goes berserk and damages the weapons console, effectively knocking out the phaser and photon torpedo controls. The ship is defenseless. Kirk orders computers to search out the word cryontha.

Meanwhile, Ilia explains the significance of pain to Irska, and adds that it is very important for her to look deeply within her own mind to discover the meaning of the mysterious word.

Kirk is desperate upon learning that all attempts at reversing the molecular breakdown of the ship have met with failure. Xon informs him that when his mind had been linked with Irska's, he got the impression that each of the near disasters which had befallen the ship were designed in such a way as to actually teach the child about life, death and

emotions. He adds that he received a sensation of incompleteness, as though an evolution was still to take place. Cryontha, whatever it may be, is the key to the next stage of her development. He suggests another mindmeld. Chekov interjects that there are only five and a half minutes left. Kirk and Xon depart to Ilia's quarters, leaving the conn to Decker. When they arrive, Ilia and Irska are in a meditative state, "sharing a sight." The Vulcan explains that this could conceivably result in the same information that the mind meld would. Within this state Ilia reacts in terror.

Kirk orders Xon to use his abilities to enter their minds and interject his theory into their line of thought. He does so and a moment later both he and Ilia are repelled from the little girl. The captain has McCoy come to their quarters. Kirk goes to get Ilia some water, and upon returning is shocked to find that Irska is gone. The security officers were so preoccupied with the Deltan and Vulcan, that they hadn't noticed her leaving.

Kirk puts all decks on alert and begins searching for Irska himself. The transporter room reports that she is there. Upon entering the room, Kirk is told by the child that cryontha translates to unnecessary shell. There are only twenty seconds left. Xon enters the room, nerve pinches the transporter technician and mans the controls. Irska runs to the platform and is transported away. The energy field leaves the Enterprise and goes back to the cylinder which, in turn, transforms into a white light energy ball similar to the one that entered the ship at the outset. Over the intercom, Chekov informs them that the hull's status is back to normal.

Xon explains that, thousands of years ago, Irska's race had existed in humanoid form. Just as a human metamorphosizes from a single cell within the mother's womb, Irska had to experience each stage of her race's prior development. Kirk is confused by this; that the child had never actually been born. Ilia responds to the point, stating that she was Irska's first womb while the Enterprise itself was her second. The captain is filled with sympathy, stating that he wishes mother and daughter could have had a longer life together, and an easier time of things.

"I appreciate your sentiments," she responds gratefully, with a beautiful smile, "but I could hardly expect you to make improvements on a miracle."

* * *

"The Child" is yet another example of just how effective a new version of *Star Trek* could have been, exploring new directions and coming up with effective storylines that would have differentiated it from the original series. Yes, we once again had the old Enterprise-in-jeopardy-with-only-a-few-seconds-left-before-destruction theme, but the reasons behind it were far more interesting. For once it wasn't Scotty or the captain or the ship's Vulcan saving the day at the final instant. This time it was completely out of their hands.

The storyline delved a bit more into the Deltan race, successfully developing the Ilia character further and proving what a valuable asset to the series she would have been. Decker still doesn't have much to do, a problem which has plagued nearly all of the scripts written for the show. This can probably be attributed to the fact that the writers could find no use for two Captain Kirks, so why not go with the original? Xon proves himself to be more likable than ever, and a fine substitute for Spock aboard the Enterprise.

In addition, this was another example of a storyline which probably would not have been possible during the 1960s. The idea of an immaculate conception and the women writhing around in such pleasure, or the basic concept of Ilia serving as a first womb and the Enterprise as the second, would have probably been too touchy for network censors. Here was evidence that *Star Trek* would continue to grow.

"TOMORROW AND THE STARS"
Written by Larry Alexander

It's obvious that the Enterprise has been involved in some kind of struggle, as there is considerable damage to the hull.

A medical log in the midst of being recorded by Dr. Leonard "Bones" McCoy informs us that the Enterprise is returning from a Klingon attack, and that there is, thankfully, only one casualty which can be considered major. His report is interrupted by screams of pain from sickbay, where we discover a delirious and wounded Chekov reliving the attack by the Federation's most fierce enemies.

Captain Kirk enters sickbay and tries to calm the weapons officer, explaining that they are in Earth orbit and he will be transported down to a radiation unit for treatment. Chekov grows more frantic and is finally given a sedative by Dr. Christine Chapel. His body goes limp, and he is brought to the transporter room, where we find Mr. Scott and Lt. Xon working on a defective demolecular circuit. Kirk is concerned, but Xon reports a probability factor for specified performance of 94.6.

Chekov is placed on the transporter platform and held in place by antigravity support. Dr. Chapel takes her position. At the last moment, a concerned McCoy examines Kirk with his medical tricorder and discovers that the captain is suffering from a mixture of fatigue and a minimal dose of irridium seven contact. He is medically ordered to spend a couple of days in detox, and he reluctantly agrees. Commander Decker is given the conn, and Kirk makes ready to leave.

The three disappear in a normal beamdown, but problems immediately arise. Chapel and Chekov reach Earth safely, but Kirk's pattern is on the verge of scattering. Both Xon and Scotty work the controls frantically, and the latter succeeds, wanting nothing more than to get the captain somewhere "retrievable." There is a mechanical and electronic shriek and the sound of high pitched voices which quickly fade, after which Xon explains that the reassembly of Captain Kirk has indeed taken place. The question is where?

A dazed Kirk shakes his head slowly as he sits on the ground of a tropical garden in a Honolulu backyard. He seems alright, except for the fact that there's a ghost like transparency about him. Trying to steady himself against a fountain, he discovers that he can't as his hand passes right through it. Tentatively he calls out for Scotty and McCoy. Finally, in an outburst, he screams, "Xon, what have you done with me?"

This is a mistake, as a door opens and Kirk darts behind some shrubbery. At the house he sees the extremely lovely Elsa Kelly, her hairstyle and the telephone she's holding definitely the style of the 1930s. Seeing no one, she goes back to her conversation. Through eavesdropping, we learn that the situation between her and her husband, Richard, is not a happy one. While she wants him to accept her father's offer to make him a vice president of his multi-million dollar company, it's obvious that he wants to make a career out of the Navy.

While this conversation takes place, Kirk unsuccessfully attempts to grab an apple (sustenance) off a tree, and eventually passes through a wall of the house to find himself in the kitchen. Still on the phone, Elsa agrees to go to an officer's party with Richard. Kirk tries to open the refrigerator and turn on the tap water, both to no avail. Elsa, having hung up, enters the kitchen and lets out a scream. Kirk pleads with her to remain calm, but she backs out of the room.

Back in engineering on the Enterprise, McCoy is chastising Xon for probably beaming the captain into the middle of an ocean somewhere. Considering that two thirds of Earth is covered in water, Xon notes, this could be quite possible, though he still has some hope. The Vulcan plays back a tape of events in the transporter room, and points out some "background" noise which is actually high-pitched voices. He attempts to use the universal translator, but the computer is unable to comply because of program erasure during the Klingon encounter.

In Honolulu, Kirk is recording a captain's log into his communicator, when Elsa returns. He is surprised, hopeful and pleased. She explains that she really doesn't believe in ghosts, so, having relaxed a bit, decided to return and find out what the situation is all about. Elsa tells him where he is, and Kirk inadvertently says that he's the commander of a "ship." He can't explain his strange uniform, but does state that he's hungry and thirsty and that if the situation continues he's going to be in serious trouble. As a car pulls into the driveway, a concerned Elsa agrees to do anything she can to help him, and Kirk "melts" back into the garden. Richard enters the house and is dismayed that she's not dressed yet, claiming that he wants to be there before the admiral arrives. She points out that ambassadors have been sent to Washington and that there's no possibility of war while talks are going on. He disagrees, stating that it's a ruse and wonders why nobody else can see it. He ends the conversation, stating that he would hate to go to the party "stag." Silently, she nods and goes to get dressed. Richard pours himself a drink, walks over to the French doors and peers out into the backyard. Instinctively, Kirk shrinks further into the greenery, wondering whether he's been spotted.

On the bridge of the Enterprise, Xon elects to use an Earthside language translator by hooking the ship's computer up to it. While the device goes to work, Sulu recognizes the language as Japanese and that the recorded conversation has something to do with two military targets, one of them an airfield between two mountain ranges.

Kirk is outside the Pearl Harbor naval base, where a sign establishes that this is the place where the party is taking place. The parking areas are filled with cars from the late 1930s and early '40s. He overhears two MPs talking about the lonely women they have to "aid" while their husbands are away.

Elsa and Richard walk out of the club in the midst of a fight. Richard claims she's been drinking far too much, and she states that she just needs some air. He wants to drive her home, but she cynically offers, "You haven't had your chat with Admiral Grant yet." Richard, it turns out, has been going through the normal protocol, the "pecking order," throughout the evening, and Elsa is not pleased. He stands there for a moment, torn between her and meeting his admiral. He chooses the latter.

Elsa walks over to the beach and across the sand, where she's spotted by the two MPs Kirk overheard earlier. The two approach Elsa, with the intent of supplying her with a little more than just aid. She begins to grow worried and asks them to let her go. They don't, while feigning innocence.

"The lady asked you to let her go," says Kirk, who has stepped out from hiding.

They whirl to see a "ghost," and take off, more frightened then they've ever been. Elsa thanks him, and states that she would like to kiss him in thanks, but it's pointless as their heads would pass through each other. She wonders if there's any way that she can get him food and water, but clearly there isn't. He questions Elsa as to the year, and discovers that it's December 6, 1941. Just as Kirk realizes the significance of the events he's been thrust into, Richard calls out

for Elsa. As she starts to leave him, Elsa asks about the significance of this date. Kirk says nothing and she goes to Richard.

In the Enterprise transporter room, Decker wants to know how this accident occurred in the first place, as the device is a transporter and not a time machine. The Vulcan explains that the fusing of electronics during the recent skirmish with the Klingons apparently created a dimensional vortex, and that Kirk has landed in the middle of Pearl Harbor right before the infamous attack by the Japanese.

The next morning, Elsa walks into her kitchen to find a frantic Kirk still unable to eat or drink anything. In his momentary panic, he accidentally reveals that he's from the future. She accepts this easily enough, and chastises him for giving up, explaining that if all he can think about is what he can't do, then he might as well be dead right now. This snaps him out of his depression.

Enterprise attempts to lock on to Kirk, and while this proves futile, it does have the beneficial effect of making him solid. He grabs Elsa in joy, and the two embrace passionately.

The next morning, during breakfast, Kirk tinkers with Richard's radio and, by hooking his wrist communicator to it, plans on trying to contact the ship. He thanks her for all the help she's provided, and explains that he's got to slip away into a crowd somewhere. They begin to kiss again, and Elsa says that she'll hide him out at home of her friend Libby, who's away for two weeks. As they drive off, Richard, who is heading home, spots them and immediately grows suspicious.

That night Elsa checks in on Kirk, who's growing frustrated again at not being able to succeed in his communication attempts. To alleviate the pressure, she suggests they take a walk on the beach. While they walk hand-in-hand, she wonders if she could accompany him back to the future, provided, of course, that he's

found. He tries to dissuade her, but they end up expressing their love for each other.

Richard picks up the communications device, and, in addressing an Intelligence Officer, states that Kirk must be either a Russian or German spy. The two men go into hiding when Kirk and Elsa return, and capture the former at gun point. While a manacled Kirk is led out to a military police car, Elsa, using her car, manages to help him escape. The MPs, including Richard, are in pursuit.

Having been successful in duplicating the transporter malfunction, Decker and McCoy materialize in the Kelly house. Tricorder readings lead them to Libby's, where they find Kirk's communicator. Another reading leads them to continue on their search.

Kirk and Elsa, who have eluded their pursuers, are hiding on a dirt road, when the captain states that it should be relatively easy to bring her back on board the Enterprise. Now she's the one having doubts; can she possibly leave behind her entire world? Despite this, she ultimately agrees to go with him, and then thinks of a good hiding place near Pearl. Kirk states that they have to stay out of the target areas. She's perplexed by this, and he goes on to explain about the imminent attack by the Japanese, and that he can't do anything about it or the course of history will be changed. Elsa grows furious at him for not revealing this information earlier. She starts to search for Richard, the love for her husband and nation suddenly welling up.

McCoy and Decker arrive on the scene, but Kirk is more concerned with Elsa, begging her to go with him. "My love for you is history," she says. "It will always be there." And with that, the men from the future are gone.

Days later, Kirk lies depressed in his cabin. McCoy and Ilia enter, with the doctor stating that he should try to forget about Elsa. Ilia disagrees, and, utilizing Deltan psychic techniques, convinces him that his life was fully enriched by Elsa's brief presence.

Kirk thanks both of them, and departs for the bridge.

* * *

"Tomorrow and the Stars" would have made a fascinating episode for the simple reason that there's always something appealing about time travel stories. Granted that in many ways this story seems a remake of "City on the Edge of Forever," it nevertheless works. Perhaps most important is that it's written with a '70s or '80s sensibility, with characters and dialogue updated dramatically.

An interesting character point is Kirk's exclaiming, "Xon, what have you done to me?" It shows the captain's prejudice against the Vulcan, as you would never, no matter the circumstance, hear him chastise Spock in this way.

"Oh yeah," laughs writer Larry Alexander, "but that's only because I was able to take it one step further. In other words, Xon is not Spock, even though I considered him Spock from a character point of view. So there is a little resentment there. It seemed the logical thing to do."

This particular script's genesis began on October 21, 1977 when Gene Roddenberry wrote a memo to Harold Livingston concerning script assignments and their schedule crisis.

"The fastest way to get some workable Star Trek scripts ready to shoot," wrote Roddenberry, "is to get some writers to work on stories we already own. Please read 'The Apartment.' Making a Star Trek episode out of it is only a rewrite."

"The Apartment" was a storyline developed for the proposed Genesis

II series, in which that show's hero, Dylan Hunt, is transported back to an apartment in the 20th Century and interacts with a woman there.

Larry Alexander was given the premise and immediately began to transfer it to the Star Trek format. What he initially came up with was an outline entitled "Ghost Story," in which Kirk and the landing team beam down to a planet that lies in ruins. There, they discover highly advanced technology, but no sign of a living civilization. Kirk enters a science lab and is projected backwards in time, where he encounters a pair of scientists. These people have developed a device to scan the mind. On a human, however, it operates quite differently. Hooked up to Kirk's brain, the machine causes him great agony. Suddenly the demons of his mind, the Id, materializes and destroys all life on the planet, thus resulting in the destruction that the crew finds in the future.

Alexander freely acknowledges the debt that "Ghost Story" owes to Forbidden Planet, but is also quick to point out that it goes beyond that film as well.

"I thought it was a wonderful story idea to have Captain Kirk responsible for the death of a planet," he enthuses, "and it's the one step beyond Forbidden Planet that had never been touched. It makes it much more human and, to me, much more of an interesting irony. That's the kind of material I think is interesting, and I was shocked when Gene Roddenberry said he didn't want to go with it."

It's suggested that maybe this wasn't the right thing to do to such a heroic character, as it would undoubtedly plague him through the rest of his life.

"In effect, it wasn't his doing," Alexander differs. "He asked them not to do it. I was very strict about that. He did not volunteer to do this, and when he realized what was going on, he did everything possible to stop it. All of that, I think, holds up on that basis. You see, I was thinking very strictly of what happened to Kirk in many episodes when things didn't turn out the way he hoped. That's what makes Star Trek so wonderful.

"As heroic as Kirk was," he continues, "through no fault of his own, hard choices had to be made. In Harlan Ellison's story, he has to allow Edith Keeler to die. It's a gulp at the end of the show, and it's like that when the people of this planet find that it's his demons which have destroyed their world and not theirs. It makes it that much more ironic."

Roddenberry preferred that Kirk go back to the Earth's past, and chose Pearl Harbor as the time and place.

"It seemed a very obvious choice," Alexander explains, "and I don't know what choice I would have gone for. Pearl Harbor is good because it's visual and you could use footage from various war films, which would work. But I didn't want to have the responsibility because the story works as a story. It's like if you send somebody back in time to kill Adolph Hitler in the crib, and he does it, the only irony you can have is his coming back and them saying, 'Why didn't you kill Kalwoski like we asked you to?' History would be the same, but somebody else would do the job.

"You want to go back in history?" Alexander concludes rhetorically. "Give me an event, and I'll do it. The story is the same no matter what."

"DEADLOCK"
Written by David Ambrose

On the bridge of the Enterprise, Commander Uhura picks up a faint distress signal identifying itself as coming from the starship Intrepid. The channel is abruptly closed. Luckily Xon had been able to lock on to coordinates, and Sulu is told to set course and proceed at maximum warp.

The Vulcan admits to Captain Kirk that he is somewhat confused by the fact that sensors have been unable to detect anything. Then the mysterious voice opens communication again, requesting that the starship come and help them. Kirk asks him to confirm his position and he does so. Xon looks up from his instruments and explains that they are apparently receiving distress signals from "no detectable source." Before Kirk can completely take in this information, Uhura states that Commodore Hunter is signaling from Starbase 7. Hunter's image appears on the main viewing screen, and the captain details to him the current situation. The commodore says that this is impossible due to the fact that the Intrepid is nowhere near the reported vicinity. Kirk is convinced that there's something out there, and would like permission to investigate. This is denied, and the Enterprise is ordered to report to Starbase 7. Emotionally torn, Kirk nonetheless follows orders. The starship departs that sector of space, the distress signal growing more faint.

The Enterprise approaches Starbase 7. Hunter's image reappears on the view screen, and he explains that Kirk and his ship are to take part in a Starfleet exercise. Kirk is furious. Were they pulled from a possible rescue mission merely to take part in some kind of game? In response, Hunter says that the exercise is already underway, and what seemed to be a distress signal actually came from a robot transmitter. All power systems are to be shut down while the Enterprise awaits further instructions.

Scotty comes up to the bridge and is asked if they can move in an emergency after the power systems are shut down. The chief engineer explains that it would take upwards of an hour to regenerate power. Kirk realizes they have to come up with a way to obey Starfleet orders without putting themselves in a position of danger. Xon punches up some equations on his computer and explains that the main reactor at a particular level coupled with boosters should allow power to be maximized within ten minutes. He adds that the system would never actually be turned off, although it would appear as though it had been. Scott agrees with this and proceeds to engineering.

Commodore Hunter reappears on the viewer and explains that Starfleet Science Advisor Lang Caradon will be instructing them from now on. Caradon comes on next and requests that all ship viewers be put into operation so that he can communicate with the entire crew. Once this is done, he states that they will all remain on ship for an unspecified amount of time in which they will have none of their regular duties. "You will, however," he says, "be required from time to time to participate in certain games. We shall wish to observe your reactions to these." He tells them to keep all communication channels open, and his image vanishes.

McCoy approaches the command chair and informs Kirk that faking a distress signal and then telling them to ignore it is a classic disorientation technique. In addition, he knows of Caradon who has been very much involved with natural response, and this whole series of games is likely to be an experiment in behavior control. The thought of serving as guinea pigs is not at all pleasing to Kirk.

Colors and random numbers begin appearing on the main viewer. Caradon asks them to guess what number will be next. An eight flashes on the screen, and two members of the bridge crew sheepishly raise a hand when asked who had guessed properly. This is repeated several times, and then the swirling colors take their place. The crew finds itself rapidly falling under the influence of hypnosis. Kirk tries to fight against this but is helpless. Xon is the only one able to resist, and while he is watching the colors he is also punching information into his computer. Then the viewer goes blank.

Ilia lets out a gasp and glances at Xon. The two lock eyes and notice that Kirk and McCoy are studying them. Xon explains that, as Kirk is well aware, Vulcans and Deltans have a certain level of telepathic abilities, and he had accidentally placed an image of captivity from his mind into hers. Xon plays back the information and sounds he had been processing into the ship's computer. Beneath the sound sent by Caradon, they hear a woman's alarmed voice shouting "Enterprise, you must escape! Report to Starfleet ... A plot – Caradon is ..." The voice "gags," as though in pain, and is replaced by static.

Kirk requests that Caradon allow him to beam over to the starbase, but he's turned down. The captain demands an explanation for the woman's voice, which he has Xon play back again. Caradon calmly states that it only took the Enterprise 24 minutes and 17 seconds to analyze the sound and respond to it. It is an excellent response time. Communication is closed.

This doesn't sit well with Kirk, despite the fact that McCoy feels that this could very well be a part of the test. Xon interjects that his research has revealed Caradon's work at the Mars laboratory was discontinued for no given reason. Glancing at the doctor, Kirk wonders if this has been an unauthorized exercise. Scotty has been able to lock onto the coordinates of the woman's voice. Kirk elects to beam over, and tells Decker that if he does not hear from him within an hour, then the commander is to board and occupy the base – even if it has to be done by force.

Kirk materializes in a storage room on Starbase 7. A door suddenly opens and the captain's eyes go wide.

Fifty minutes later on the Enterprise, Decker is ordering the boarding party to the transporter room. Just as this instruction is about to be carried out, Kirk's image appears on the viewscreen. The captain informs them that he is convinced everything that has occurred is indeed a part of the exercise. He is about to add another point, but abruptly says they should all continue to cooperate fully. Decker asks Kirk when he will be beaming back, and is told that it will not happen until after the exercise is complete. The viewer goes black.

McCoy and Decker are both uneasy and would have been much more convinced if they had spoken to Kirk face to face rather than over the viewscreen. The commander is finding it hard to believe that Kirk would succumb so easily to pressure. McCoy suggests that hypnosis or any of a number of drugs could have been used to alter his thinking.

In a control booth on the starbase, an unconscious Kirk lies on a surgical table with scanning instruments hovering over him. The captain revives and finds himself staring into the face of Lieutenant Commander Anderson. Kirk is told that the commodore is attending a conference at Starfleet headquarters and won't be available for another week. Anderson says that because of the captain and his crew's recent behavior, there is no choice but to keep him restrained until they can find out exactly what's going on. Kirk wants to know if this is another of Caradon's exercises. Anderson claims that he has no idea what Kirk is talking about.

Anderson explains that five days earlier the starbase had received a message from the Enterprise that they had entered an unexplored area of

space and were suffering from a mysterious virus. Kirk himself had requested they return to Starbase 7 so that the crew could be assisted. As proof, a log of Kirk making this request is played on the viewscreen. A second image replaces it and Kirk desperately tries to convince the other man that it has somehow been faked. His pleas are fruitless.

Back on the Enterprise, Xon believes that a link-up between a transmitter and a central computer could conceivably fake such a message by reprogramming stored data. He presents a demonstration of this theory on the viewscreen by showing a slightly different image of the bridge crew. They're stunned by this. The "image Kirk," phaser in hand, fires at the images of Decker and Xon before the screen goes black. McCoy wonders if the Vulcan finds this amusing.

"On the contrary," Xon differs, "I am alarmed at how easily we can be misled by our own inventions."

McCoy suggests that they beam over with a full boarding party, but Decker states that they still need proof. He and Xon will beam over. If there is no contact within half an hour, Scott is to take command of the base. Only personal contact is to be accepted.

A 10 member landing party begins to beam over, and as they do so alarm klaxons sound on the starbase. A security detail is sent to meet the boarders. The guards run toward what looks like rematerializing figures, but they fade away again. This happens several times as Scotty operates the transporter, performing his own form of "exercise." The Duty Officer informs Anderson that the images were all decoys, because no one beamed over from the Enterprise. Xon and Decker finally do beam over, however.

Anderson has deflectors raised, and announces that as of this moment the Enterprise is to be considered a hostile vessel. In response, Scotty

raises deflectors. McCoy is outraged by all that is happening and would like to know why everybody's deflectors are up and why they're about to attack one of their own starbases. Scott doesn't have the answer, which, he points out, is exactly what they're fighting for.

Decker and Xon make their way to the isolation room and see Kirk through the glass partition. The commander signals for him to remain silent while Xon, combining phaser beam and communication frequencies, manages to short-circuit the force field keeping Kirk prisoner. The three make a run for it. Starbase guards detect the break and begin a pursuit.

As guards approach, Decker sets his phaser on stun and gives it to Kirk. They manage to knock out two guards, and take their phasers. Now all three are armed. Xon, who had studied a plan for the base before beaming over, states that they should make their way to the central computer relay station so that they can shut down the force field surrounding the base. They make their way to the center and phaser seal the door behind them. Kirk hopes that it will give them enough time to find out exactly what's been happening. A voice tells him that he has already done so.

The trio turn around to find Commodore Hunter. He congratulates them on their initiative, as does Caradon, who emerges from between the bank of computers. Kirk is suspicious and raises his phaser, telling them to stand exactly where they are.

In the control room, Anderson orders the security guards to burn their way through the sealed doors. He has controls switched to manual override while there's still time before the Enterprise trio sabotage the weapons system.

Back in the relay center, Kirk fires his phaser and the beams go right through Hunter and Caradon. They transform into ghost-like beings who reveal that the Federation is approaching their territory and that they are extremely concerned about it. It is their intention to create hostilities amongst the humans so that they will eventually destroy themselves and are never able to infect their part of the galaxy. The Caradon alien, who explains that he and his counterpart have merely assumed the guise of the humans who are elsewhere, says that members of their people have already fallen under "the influence of primitive, violent emotions and thought emanations from your race."

Decker points out that man controls his darker nature with reason. The aliens claim that this control is, at best, tenuous. Kirk is angered by all this, demanding to know if turning the humans against each other is their idea of morality. The Hunter alien says that their fate is in their own hands, and the two of them disappear. Communication can suddenly be conducted between the Enterprise and the starbase. Decker notes that in 11 minutes Scotty will authorize an armed boarding party to beam over . . . right into the trap that has been set for them: both Starbase 7 and the Enterprise are making preparations to attack each other.

Guards break into the Relay Center and surround Kirk, Decker and Xon before the Vulcan has had the opportunity to deactivate the base's phasers. They're taken to the control room, where Kirk attempts to explain to Anderson exactly what has been going on. Anderson, naturally, does

not believe a word of it. After much pleading, Kirk finally convinces him to allow contact with the Enterprise. Kirk warns Scotty not to move the ship or the base will open fire. Scott is uneasy with this, claiming that this is merely another trap. Anderson thinks the same thing, but Kirk wants to know why he would plan an attack while he and the others are on the starbase. Anderson comes up with a reason, much to Kirk's exasperation.

Xon speaks to Lt. Ilia, asking her to receive the impressions of thoughts in his mind. She recites a formula designed earlier by Xon. This is evidence enough as there was no way for the Deltan to have known this on her own. Scott lowers the ship's deflectors and Anderson disarms phasers. Peace between them has been obtained.

In the story's final Captain's Log, Kirk recommends that no starship enter the nearby alien territory until invited to do so. He states that his only hope is that "whatever influence they continue to feel from us will be felt in a more positive light as a result of our demonstrated, if somewhat tenuous, self control."

* * *

"Deadlock" begins as a highly imaginative suspense thriller with no one really knowing what's true and what's false. The idea of training exercises "gone wrong" is an intriguing one, but unfortunately we are once again confronted with an alien intelligence

that is so offended by our barbaric streak that they feel it is their duty to destroy us. We've seen it before. As a result, a highly creative idea gets diluted to repetitive status towards the conclusion of the story.

It's quite possible that author David Ambrose should not be held accountable for this situation as the whole concept of "gods" striking against man is an old standby used by Gene Roddenberry many times in the past, and his influence can be felt here. Supporting this statement is the fact that on September 14, 1977 Ambrose had submitted a treatment entitled "All Done With Mirrors," which was essentially the same story with a different resolution. In the treatment, a very human Caradon was acting on his own accord. He explains that he is part of an underground organization which plans to overthrow the Federation. This struggle between a flagship and a starbase would be the first blow struck. Many more "accidents" of this nature would follow, and be aided by a variety of "dedicated fanatics" in key Starfleet positions willing to sacrifice their lives for the cause.

While lacking the science fiction trappings of the script, this final point would have made a far more effective conclusion, concurrently stating that not everything is as it appears in Starfleet. To this writer's mind, a human threat in this manner is far more creative than just one more angered alien race.

"KITUMBA"
Written by John Meredyth Lucas

"Kitumba" begins with the Enterprise enroute to Starfleet Command, where they are to pick up a radiation burn victim. Both Kirk and Decker are miffed at this, wondering why the Enterprise is being used for such a task when tensions are high in that part of the galaxy.

Kirk, McCoy and the transporter technician, are adorned in radiation suits, watching as Admiral Li materializes. She immediately explains that their outfits won't be necessary, and then, much to the doctor's chagrin, he and the technician are asked to leave. Kirk doesn't protest.

Once they're alone, Li explains that this facade was used because something "big" and top secret is going on. It seems that Federation Intelligence Drones have detected starships locking in orbit around hundreds of Klingon subject planets, and fears are high that there will be an imminent "overwhelming" attack.

Kirk remains puzzled as Li has her passenger beamed up. He is a Klingon named Ksia, tutor to the Sacred Ruler of his people, the Kitumba. Li explains that Ksia has warned the Federation that the Klingons plan on launching a secret strike.

"If it were true," Kirk asks Ksia, "why would you tell us?"

"We are not properly prepared for war at this time," Ksia replies simply.

Through the ensuing conversation, we learn that the name Klingon is applicable only to the ruling warrior class. The Techos, consisting of both scientists and technicians, are a sociological level below them, and the people on the following level, the great masses, are known as the Subjects. The Kitumba, although considered a God-King, is little more than a figurehead. The Empire, in actuality, is ruled by the Warlord.

Ksia explains that Kitumba means "the power," and that he never leaves the Sacred Planet, which is located at the very center of their Empire. All of the planets belong to him, but the power is channeled through the Warlord. The problem is that the Kitumba is a 17-year-old boy, while the current Warlord, Malkthon, is the one planning to attack the Federation. "Incredible as is the power Malkthon has built," says Ksia, "war between the Federation and the Klingon Empire could only result in mutual annihilation."

Kirk's assignment, as incredible as it seems, is to take the Enterprise to the Sacred Planet within the Klingon Empire, so that they can meet with the Kitumba and, hopefully, avert the war. Ksia will do his best to help them in this task, and they realize they have no choice but to accept his aid. Once the Klingon submits to a medical exam by McCoy, Li explains that, no matter what the consequences, the Enterprise must be detonated before being allowed to fall into enemy hands.

On the bridge, Ilia is using her Delta charms, which are definitely affecting Ksia. He explains that women in his society bear children between ages 21 and 29. Those 30 and above care for the children until they are aged six. At that point, the youths begin warrior training.

"Not unlike some of the ancient cultures of Earth. The Spartans, for instance," adds Xon, in the first of several examples of his keen interest in Terran history.

As the Enterprise moves through space at warp speed, sensors indicate a Klingon "ghost ship" which, Ksia emphasizes, must be destroyed before it can report their position. After a chase, photon torpedoes find their mark.

"He died well," Ksia says with pride.

"I'm sorry," replies a stunned Kirk. "It was necessary."

The ship nears the Neutral Zone, where sensors detect five Klingon battle cruisers. Ksia transmits a message claiming that the Federation is attacking planet Gamma 35. The cruisers begin moving towards that planet at warp speed. With that particular obstacle removed, the Enterprise proceeds at warp factor six.

On the viewer in the briefing room is the image of the Sacred Planet. Ksia explains that there are no defenses around the world. The humans are amazed by this. The Klingon says that Xon had shown him Earth history tapes, and that, in the past, there had been similar conditions. "During the period of the Roman Empire's greatest expansion," concurs the Vulcan, "the city had no walls. The Romans' proudest boast was that her legions were her walls."

Walls or no, Kirk points out that there will be numerous Klingon starships between them and the Sacred Planet. Ksia adds that if the Enterprise should reach that world's orbit, it will be granted sanctuary.

Shortly thereafter, a number of vessels move in for the kill. Kirk manages to elude them and then, in a rather brilliant move, has Ilia use her Esper abilities to read the image of the proper star system from Ksia's mind and, in turn, program the coordinates into the ship's computer. In an additional burst of energy, the Enterprise is on the proper path.

They successfully reach their goal. Kirk opens communications with the quite beautiful Taru, Deputy Warlord, who reluctantly grants them sanctuary. However, she does warn him that sanctuary has its rules, as the traitor Ksia can tell him. The captain explains that they would like an audience with the Kitumba to offer respect and to assure the peaceful intent of the Federation. Taru will forward their request to Malkthon, and they will be informed of his response.

A full day later there is still no response, but Ksia is confident that the

Kitumba will grant them an audience for the simple reason that he will be anxious to see the face of the enemy. Taru finally opens communications and gives the affirmative. Kirk will beam down, unarmed with the exception of perhaps a ceremonial weapon.

Decker suggests his ceremonial sword from his Academy full dress uniform.

"I had one, too," responds Kirk wryly. "We used them, principally, for cutting cake."

Ksia notes that the sword would nonetheless make a better impression than beaming down without anything at all. The Klingon hands Kirk a dagger which is to be given to Baro Kali, who will stand to the right of the Kitumba. He will be recognized by a lightning-shaped scar on his forehead. The captain should announce that this dagger of a Klingon killed honorably in battle is being offered to the Kitumba as a gift. In actuality, Kali is the head of the Peace Party, and the dagger contains a message.

Before transporting down, Kirk reminds Decker that the Enterprise engines should be imploded before surrender. With that, he's gone.

Kirk bows before the Kitumba, while the Klingons in the room prostrate themselves before their ruler. The human explains that it is the hope of his people to avoid an intergalactic conflict, and that this meeting will develop into peaceful cooperation. Kirk offers the dagger to the Kitumba, who, in turn, gives permission for Kali to accept it.

"I am pleased my son died well," says Kali as he takes the weapon. "Were you the victor?"

"It was not my honor," replies Kirk.

The Kitumba says that he will honor it, and with that the audience comes to an end.

Enterprise: Ksia explains that when Kali is ready to see Kirk, a fire will break out in the Subject section of the city. For that, the starship captain must be adorned in Subject clothing. The Klingon also says that at the time of the old Kitumba's death, Malkthon seized power as Klingon Warlord.

"Captain," queries Xon, "is it realistic to hope to convince a 17-year-old boy to stand against the incredible power Malkthon has amassed?"

Before Kirk responds, Ksia says that if their plan fails, the Federation must attack Ultar, the Warlord home world, so that Malkthon's strength can be broken without destroying the Empire. "The Federation would never agree to a first strike," interjects Kirk. "More important – our mission is to prevent war."

Later Kirk beams down to the Subject city to meet with Kali. Ksia remains behind, because he may never touch the soil of the Sacred Planet again due to the "dishonor" he has brought upon himself.

During their conversation, Kali suggests, without actually saying, that the possibility exists Malkthon killed the former Kitumba, thus paving his own way to power. In addition, he believes that Kirk may be able to influence the current Kitumba because he could be more insistent than the average Klingon. "Once the power has spoken," he says, "the matter is closed. If we have incurred his slightest displeasure, we must Remove – commit suicide."

The Kitumba, it seems, occasionally sneaks into the Subject city, and is currently doing so. They go to a bar. The Kitumba is at the end of the bar, with two lovely women. He takes notice of Kali, and, a bit saddened, leaves his female companions. Kali rushes his ruler outside, where he meets with Kirk.

"It must be quick," warns Kali. "You're in danger here." Kirk flips open his communicator. "Scotty, now!" He and the Kitumba are transported aboard the Enterprise. Kali is furious, feeling betrayed by the humans.

Kirk opens communications with Kali, and informs him that the Kitumba is safe and will be returned shortly. As they move on to the bridge, the Kitumba is amazed to see the diversity of aliens. "We've learned to work together," smiles Kirk.

Xon gives the Klingon ruler a brief sample of Federation history, and something of a tour takes place. Kirk eventually realizes that too much time has passed, but before the Kitumba is beamed down he feels that there is one more thing the ruler should see.

Ksia prostrates himself before the Kitumba, and a look of an old friendship passes between them. Ksia explains that he brought the aliens so that all their people could be saved. "This war Malkthon wishes," he says, "would destroy both cultures. The alien will teach you." With that said, he asks if the ruler would "witness." The teenager nods, and Ksia activates a wrist device which disintegrates the older Klingon. Kirk is stunned with horror.

"After what he did," Kirk explodes, "all he went through for you, you killed him!"

The Kitumba dismisses this outburst. The reason Ksia Removed is because he broke the law. Nonetheless, he died with honor and his name may be spoken again.

Kirk and the Kitumba beam down to the alley, where Kali stands with two swords pressed against his throat. Kirk immediately attempts to contact Scotty, but the communicator is knocked from his hand and a sword placed at his throat. The Kitumba orders Kirk taken to the Sacred Palace, because there is much they can learn from him.

On the Enterprise, Scotty is fearful that the captain has either been killed or is a prisoner. Xon suggests that, with the exception of his ears, he looks the most like a Klingon and should beam down. After a moment's hesitation, Decker agrees.

"They'll eat him alive," warns Scotty.

"There is no indication in our records that the Klingons are cannibals," replies Xon with a raised eyebrow.

In the Sacred Palace, Kirk continues his attempts to sway the Kitumba to his way of thinking. All it will take is one word from him to stop Malkthon. The Kitumba is obviously torn by conflicting emotions.

Once beam down is complete, Xon is nearly captured by a Klingon, but he uses a variation of the Vulcan nerve pinch, which paralyzes the other man. Xon orders the Klingon to take him to Kali. He obeys. Meanwhile, Taru, on her authority, orders Kirk to be killed in his cell. A pair of Klingons attack, but Kirk pretty much dispatches them. Taru moves in for the kill, but is stopped by the now furious Kitumba. "How dare my prisoner be attacked!"

"Forgive me, Lord, I had no idea the alien was under your protection. Shall I Remove?"

He doesn't respond, and Taru leaves the room to contact Malkthon, explaining that the human is now under the Kitumba's protection. Malkthon is enraged. "He is not under mine. Kill him."

Xon is led to Kali's home by his prisoner, and Kali lets the Vulcan in after he identifies himself. Still holding the Klingon at bay with the nerve pinch, Xon uses his mental abilities to make the man forget their encounter and return to the tavern. The Klingon does so. Kali explains that Malkthon's plans are to spread the Klingon sphere of influence throughout the galaxy. He is also attempting to arrange a non-aggression treaty with the Romulans, who have sent a delegation to Ultar. Malkthon's goal is to crush the Federation and then attack the Romulans.

Decker contacts Xon, stating that a Klingon warship has locked into orbit. Kali explains that it must be Malkthon, asking the Kitumba to give the order for battle. Kali decides to take Xon to the Sacred Palace.

Malkthon kneels before the Kitumba, asking him to approve the imminent "glorious" war with his sacred seal. The youth replies that he will study the order and advise him. He walks out of the room. Malkthon stares at Taru, enraged.

Kali and Xon make it to Kirk's cell, where they inform the captain that the battle fleets are moving. The Klingon fears that Malkthon's first action may be to kill Kirk so that the Kitumba's opinion will remain "unclouded."

To put his plan into effect, Malkthon makes an exact duplicate of Kirk's ceremonial sword.

"It's a toy," says Taru with disgust.

"This toy will win the war for us."

Kali manages to get Kirk and Xon into the Kitumba's chambers. The Klingon kneels before him, begging for the opportunity to speak. Kali sees that the youth is troubled. "I don't know who to trust," admits the frightened Kitumba, "what to believe." He explains that Malkthon has sent the Prince, the Kitumba's six-year-old brother, to Ultar. The ruler was not asked for approval, and can't understand why not.

Kirk deduces that a six-year-old Kitumba would be considerably more controllable. A knock comes upon the door and the captain goes into hiding. A Klingon guard enters, telling his ruler that Malkthon requests a private audience. The Kitumba agrees, but in a little while. As soon as the guard leaves, Kali adds that Malkthon will want him to approve the war.

"And you say I shouldn't."

"It's what Ksia said," Kirk interjects. "What he died for. It's what I say."

They beam aboard the Enterprise to formulate a plan. Xon suggests that since he is about the same size and shape as the Kitumba, perhaps he should impersonate the Klingon. Superior hearing and discernment will allow him to duplicate his voice, while the power of suggestion should do the rest.

Xon/Kitumba meets with Malkthon. During their conversation, Malkthon pulls out the duplicate of Kirk's sword and thrusts it through the "Kitumba's" heart. The body falls to the floor. Taru enters, and Malkthon informs her that the alien captain has murdered their lord. "I go to Ultar to proclaim the new Kitumba!"

They leave the room. Kirk and Kali run to Xon. Taru sees them and orders the imprisonment of both. Kali protests, telling her to watch the visual record. She is horrified to see Malkthon kill the Kitumba. Taru will no longer serve the Warlord, and for this shame she feels they should all Remove.

"No," shouts Kirk. "Stop wasting lives. Malkthon's the only one who must be Removed." He contacts Scotty and has Xon's body beamed back to the Enterprise.

Taru tries to enter the communications room to contact the Fleet, but the guards arrest her and Kali, as Malkthon has said anybody attempting such communication is guilty of treason.

Kirk has Scotty beam him a phaser, and he stuns the two guards. He and Taru enter the room, but then realize they don't have the secret code needed for the transmission. "Well," sighs Kirk, "we've certainly burned our bridges here." The three beam up.

The situation is desperate. They can't break orbit as normal for fear they will be destroyed, and they can't remain or Malkthon's war will take place. Kirk comes up with a plan: they'll have to jump out of orbit at warp speed and beam the Kitumba aboard the Klingon flagship when they are in range.

While this is put into action, Kirk visits sickbay and is told by McCoy that Xon will be fine, for the simple reason that, unlike humans and Klingons, the Vulcan heart is on the right side.

The Enterprise breaks orbit at

warp speed and heads towards its objective. There are blasts fired from Klingon vessels and some damage to shields takes place, but they are able to beam the Kitumba aboard the Klingon flagship, with Kirk noting, "It's all up to you."

Klingon cruisers move in for the kill, but the attack breaks off. The Kitumba appears on the viewscreen, explaining that hostilities have ceased, and the battle group is under his personal command. He and Captain Kalem beam aboard the Enterprise.

From Ultar, Malkthon transmits the news that the Kitumba has been assassinated by the Federation captain, and that power has descended upon Prince Klun.

The Klingons on board the Enterprise modify the ship's power system to temporarily emit a cloaking screen. Enterprise, at this point invisible, approaches Ultar with a hundred Klingon vessels. Malkthon wants every disruptor aimed on the incoming fleet. Taru contacts him, explaining that the Earth vessel has been destroyed and they wish to join the glorious war. He agrees.

Xon beams down to the surface and meets with the Romulan delegation attempting to convince them of the reality of the situation. He is successful, and they, too, attack the Klingons on the planet.

A savage fist fight takes place between Kirk and Malkthon, in which the human is finally victorious. The Kitumba and his brother enter the room, announcing that Malkthon is removed from power and is to be considered an outlaw. In addition, he recalls the battle fleets. Malkthon requests permission to Remove. "No," Kirk protests, "that's too easy. Have him tried for treason. Imprisoned." The Kitumba ignores this, and gives permission. Malkthon disintegrates.

Later, Kirk says that maybe the time has come for their races to have peace, trade and friendship.

"It is enough we have no war,"

replies the Kitumba. "The rest must wait."

Kirk admits that he doesn't like partial victories. "Captain," points out Xon, "you were told to stop a war, not create an alliance."

"People and habits take a long while to change," says the Kitumba. "But to you, personally, I shall be grateful."

Kirk nods, accepting this. He and the Kitumba share a look of friendship and admiration. Kirk and Xon bow, and depart.

* * *

Of all the scripts written for the *Star Trek II* television series, it is probably "Kitumba" that would still make the most promising feature film, delving into an area previously unexplored. Although, in a sense, this story can be viewed as something of a prequel to the events of the feature film, *Star Trek VI: The Undiscovered Country*.

The Klingons had been used on a variety of *Star Trek* episodes, but never to as great an effect as they would have been here. To his credit, John Meredyth Lucas has taken previously established information and expanded upon it to such a degree that he has created a very real and tangible Klingon society.

In the "Errand of Mercy" episode of the original series, one of the Organians stated that some day both the Federation and the Klingons would become good friends. "Kitumba" at least suggests that both are slowly moving towards that goal; a goal obviously met in the era of *The Next Generation*. In particular, one would imagine that there could be a continuing friendship of some sort between Kirk and the Kitumba.

Insofar as *Star Trek II* is concerned, this script also manages to give us a bit of a handle on the new characters. The Klingons who meet Lt. Ilia are instantly affected by her sexual hormones, so predominant in Deltans, and we are given keen examples of Xon's mental and physical abilities.

Being a full Vulcan, he is even more powerful than Spock was, and, as such, has quite a few fascinating talents. The only foreseeable problem with this is that future scriptwriters likely would have given Xon even more extensive abilities, which, in turn, would have made it as necessary to get rid of him in many episodes as it would be to knock the power out of the Enterprise. It would be the only way to create real jeopardy.

Will Decker has a particularly good moment, which was not included in the preceding synopsis:

Scotty warns that the "Odds against our mission are . . . "

"We don't need the odds against," snaps Decker. "Do all you can for us."

"You sound just like the captain."

"Thank you, Mr. Scott."

A nice touch.

Producer Harold Livingston's reaction to "Kitumba" was immediate, and on October 26, 1977 he shot a note off to writer John Meredyth Lucas, which read, in part, "I think it's very exciting, visually interesting and dramatic. It should be one hell of a show. The enclosed notes are really very minor points, if they get in your way just disregard them. They're rather unimportant, which illustrates the excellent flow of the story, so go with it and good luck."

Lucas himself is justifiably proud of this particular effort. "I wanted something that we'd never seen before on the series," he says, "and that's a penetration deep into enemy space. I then started to think of how they lived. Obviously for the Romulans we had Romans, and we've had different cultures modeled on those of ancient earth, but I tried to think of what the Klingon society would be like. The Japanese came to mind, so, basically, that's what it was, with the Sacred Emperor, the Warlord, and so on."

"ARE UNHEARD MELODIES SWEET?"
Written by Worley Thorne

The Enterprise is scanning a planet in the Hyades star cluster in search of the vanished starship St. Louis. A landing party has beamed down, searching for some sign that perhaps the vessel had entered the atmosphere and there were survivors.

Xon informs Kirk that they are still detecting humanoid life forms other than the search team. The captain wants Uhura to open communication with Decker. Once this is done, the first officer informs him that ship's scanners must be malfunctioning, for he can detect no inhabitants on the planet's surface. Xon suggests that this is a possibility, since they "have been subjecting the equipment to 24-hour punishment these last weeks." Kirk concurs, telling Decker that they will get back to him shortly.

On the planet's surface, Rand's tricorder detects artificial materials deep within a hill. She and Decker phaser blast a hole and proceed through it. They find "smooth, twisted metallic plastic," and other pieces which prove they were driven into the hill "at high speed under tremendous heat and pressure." The theory is that these are some of the remains of the St. Louis. The pieces are beamed aboard the Enterprise, where Xon informs Kirk that scanners are operating perfectly, and is told to report to the lab to study the pieces of material just beamed aboard.

Ensigns Kelly and Ibsen discover a lake filled with bare breasted and lovely natives. The two men strip and begin frolicking with the women. A closeup of one of the women reveals that her eyes are "unnaturally large, glowing, luminous."

Kirk finds it hard to believe that these pieces are what remains of the St. Louis, which is what Xon is stating. The captain's argument is that a fully fueled starship with no reported mis-

haps under the guidance of a captain like Michael Schwerner could not have merely burned up in the planet's atmosphere. The analysis continues.

An interesting bit of dialogue follows, effectively capturing a bit of characterization as well as stating Kirk's frame of mind throughout this mission.

"Captain Kirk, I am working on it," states Xon evenly. "Anything I said now would be less than conjecture."

"Then conjecture," Kirk replies. "You are, reputedly, the boy wonder."

"Jim . . . Jim. Mike Schwerner is a close friend . . ." interjects McCoy. "My closest, present company of course excluded. But if you're going to help him, you've got to be less . . . 'involved.'"

"If I'm going to help him, I have to know all the possibilities. My apologies, Mr. Xon, if I seemed too much the devil's advocate."

Xon is confused. "I do not understand your apology, Captain. In your elder, human terms, 'boy wonder' is an approximately correct phrase, but I have as yet supplied no conjectures. Perhaps I should apologize?"

"You're doing a fine job, Lieutenant."

This shows a bit of an obsession on Kirk's part, as well as the continuing relationship between Bones and the captain and the sarcastic/slight resentment he has towards Spock's replacement.

Decker makes his way up a sandy dune, and suddenly finds himself in a beautiful flowered park. He walks by a rock with a large plaque set in it that reads "Mariners Park-United Federation of Planets-Starfleet Academy." This is an exact memory from 14 years earlier. He snaps on his wrist communicator, but doesn't say anything as a lovely 20-year-old girl he knew named Linda approaches and embraces him. Unknowingly to him, her eyes become luminous and he suddenly looks somewhat

younger, finding himself dressed in his Starfleet Academy uniform. Their passion grows.

Picking up Decker's communication channel, the bridge crew hears the rustling of clothes being taken off and the sound of Decker talking to someone . . . but who? His is the only voice that they hear. A moment later, they realize they're listening to the commander making love, and giggles can be heard from the crew. Kirk stops such reactions immediately. He and McCoy agree that it sounds as though Decker is speaking "post-adolescent drivel." Something is definitely amiss. The transporter locks onto his coordinates and beams him aboard. "Linda" moves away from him and, as he disappears, the park transforms into its true image: that of an alien city. Linda becomes a beautiful exotic alien named Ronel.

Decker is extremely apologetic to Kirk, who he refers to as sir, pointing out that he "should be in class." It seems that the commander truly believes that he is a midshipman at the Academy. Even his uniform, to his own eyes at least, is that of a cadet's. Bones is at a loss as to what's happening, pointing out that there is nothing foreign in Decker's body. The commander is restricted to quarters, with a security guard just outside the door.

Returning to the bridge, Kirk is informed by Xon that among the wreckage discovered on the planet is a part of the captain's log. Electronically enhancing the remaining signal, they place the somewhat clouded image of Captain Michael Schwerner on the viewing screen. According to the log, the St. Louis crashed into the atmosphere five days earlier, and the cause, says Schwerner, was that the crew was experiencing some sort of delirium and set the ship's instruments awry. Kirk and McCoy entertain the fear that perhaps the delirium is some sort of plague-like illness.

Later, Ronel materializes on the transporter platform, but technician

Probably the strongest element of the original *Star Trek* was the relationship between Kirk and Spock. In Robert Silverberg's proposed feature film *The Billion Year Voyage*, the duo would have become even closer via an alien technology that would enable the users to share a communal mind.
(photo copyright © 1994 G. Trindl/Shooting Star)

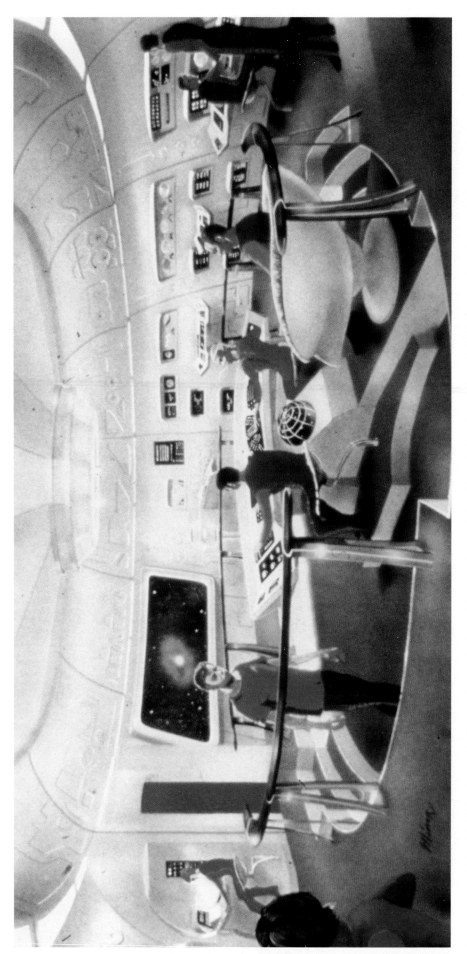

The bridge of the refurbished starship Enterprise as designed for the aborted *Star Trek II* television series of 1977. As can be discerned, this version of the bridge was conceived to be roomier than the one created for the original series. While not on a level with *The Next Generation* in terms of its Holiday Inn type of quality, it nonetheless was more comfortable than the first bridge.

There are more stations than on the first series, and the globe in front of Kirk's command chair was originally conceived to project holographic star maps, a notion that was dropped when the series became *Star Trek: The Motion Picture*. The railing around the bridge would be shortened by about half when the films went into production. (conceptual sketch courtesy Mike Minor)

In the original conception of the *Star Trek II* series, there was going to be an attempt to get more into the private lifestyles of Enterprise crewmembers. Instead of just seeing how they handle battle situations or exploring strange new worlds, the audience would have seen them at play.

In this design for the ship's rec room, we see various crewmembers relaxing, a couple perhaps engaging in an intimate conversation and others playing some sort of anti-gravity games. (conceptual sketch courtesy Mike Minor)

The cast of the original series signed up for the proposed syndicated *Star Trek II*, with the sole exception of Leonard Nimoy who was involved in a legal action against Paramount Pictures regarding the studio's use of his likeness in Trek merchandise without compensating him. When it became clear that this situation would not be worked out, and given his blossoming career, Nimoy refused to sign on the dotted line.

In his place was New York actor David Geautraux as Lieutenant Xon, one of three new characters created for the series. Unlike Spock, Xon was a full Vulcan who had his own set of problems in terms of working with humans. While the human-Vulcan hybrid Spock fought an inner war between his emotional and logical halves, Xon wanted to gain a better understanding of humanity and actually sought out – with great difficulty – his emotions. Also working within the character was the fact that he had to live up to Kirk's expectations – which were a lot, given the captain's relationship with Spock – and his banter with Dr. McCoy.

When the studio decided to make a feature instead, the actor dropped out of the firm, refusing to diminish the character's integrity to that of a cameo. Instead, he portrayed Commander Branch of the Epsilon Nine space station, ultimately doomed by the arriving V'ger. (photo courtesy David Gautreaux)

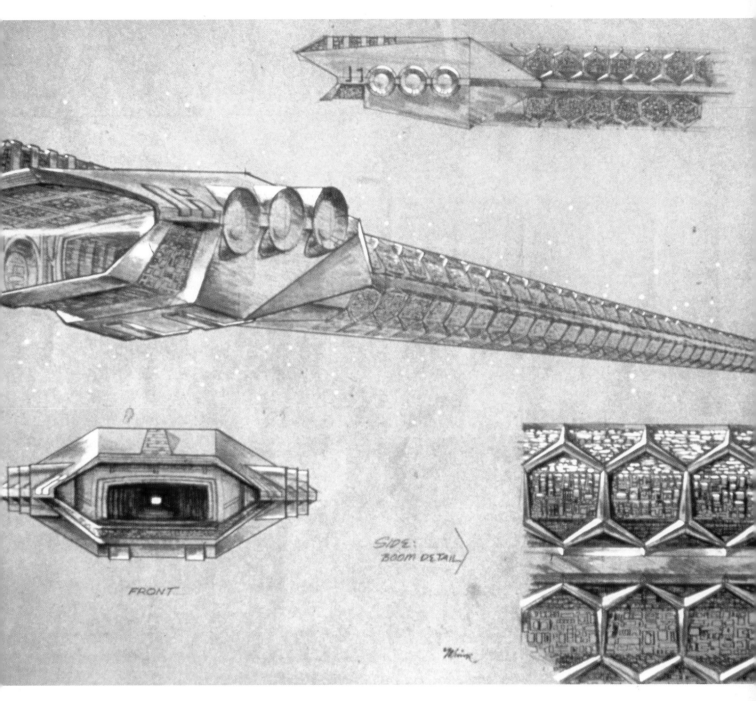

This was the original conception of V'ger, the returning Voyager 6 space probe that had achieved consciousness and was coming back to Earth to physically join with its creator, NASA. As is obvious, that first design – rather than the luminous cloud that would be seen in *Star Trek: The Motion Picture* – was pretty much a tunnel in space, harkening back to the original series episode "The Doomsday Machine." In comparing the two, one would see that this is just a more streamlined version of that concept. (conceptual sketch courtesy Mike Minor)

A highlight of both the first proposed episode of *Star Trek II* ("In Thy Image") and *Star Trek: The Motion Picture*, was a view of the refurbished Enterprise in space dock. Here, toward the lower right, you can see the massive starship held in place by the space dock. Toward the right, there is a space station and a shuttle approaching the Enterprise, presumably the one bringing Kirk and Scotty to the starship so they can get on their way in the combatting of the V'ger threat. Behind all three items is Earth.
(conceptual sketch courtesy Mike Minor)

The first F/X house of *Star Trek: The Motion Picture* attempted to provide some scope of V'ger, by having a relatively tiny Enterprise being pulled in to the alien creation. Robert Abel & Associates, as has been well documented, was ultimately replaced by John Dysktra and Douglas Trumbull.

Besides Xon, the other alien on board the Enterprise was Lieutenant Ilia, the helmsman who was actually an empathic Deltan. As conceived for *Star Trek II*, Ilia would have been a regular character but given the nature of the feature films, there seemed to be plenty of characters around from the original cast, so she wasn't seen as necessary.

Escobar sees her as Rand. Her eyes glow luminously, and he signals an alert. She enters Decker's quarters as McCoy, and transforms into Linda. Decker is immediately euphoric, stating that they'll escape from this place together. Catching the guard by surprise, Decker knocks him out and runs down the corridor with Linda. Eluding security, they make their way into engineering, dispatch a few people stationed there and manage to drain the engine coolant system and destroy the dilithium crystals powering the vessel. Ronel becomes Kirk as "he" and Decker beam back down to the planet's surface.

Scotty fills Kirk in on how severe the damage is, and they realize that their situation is mirroring that of the St. Louis. There are six, maybe seven, hours before the Enterprise spirals into the atmosphere and meets its demise. Ilia states that the St. Louis had obtained a large supply of unrefined dilithium, and there is the slightest possibility that some of it managed to survive re-entry due to its shielding. No matter how dangerous these crystals may be, if they exist at all, Kirk realizes that it's a risk they're going to have to take.

Kirk, McCoy and Ilia, having beamed down, discover a monolith containing sophisticated equipment to synthesize food from the air and soil, but, as McCoy points out, the machinery is decayed and breaking down.

They notice a dozen or so aliens dancing ritualistically, and one of them collapses by the trio's feet – apparently having been beaten to death, although no one touched her.

"Group killing by illusion," Kirk muses.

The captain abruptly finds himself in a fantasy where he has just made love to Ronel.

"Is any of this real?" he asks.

"Is that so important?" she replies seductively. "I offer you a feast of sensation . . . without rejection, or jealousy or guilt."

He partially manages to snap himself out of this illusion, demanding to know what Ronel wants of them. Her reply is for him to have his crew transported down so they can experience this paradise as well. Kirk tells her that they don't have enough power left for that – perhaps if she would help him get the necessary dilithium. Ronal says she must report to the Council, and Kirk finds himself back with McCoy and Ilia. It turns out that all three of them had been engaged in their own private fantasies.

Ronel reappears and takes them to the Council building. The Council explains that everyone on Grokhoor is "free to do as they please," which is why the society is on the verge of ruin. They are studying the Enterprise's reactions to their illusionary abilities. The humans are needed for something . . . .but a complete explanation is not forthcoming. Ronel cryptically adds that they will not make the same mistake that they did with the crew of the St. Louis.

In a laboratory, the trio, phasers drawn, discover Ibsen, Kelly and Rand on slabs with IV tubes connected to them. Despite this, it is obvious that they're involved in some sort of delusion. Moments later, Ibsen is dead, a victim of "over stimulation." Moving on, they find Decker and realize that he's dying as well. They deduce that the Grokhoor's illusionary powers could create fantasies so exciting that they're beyond human capacity to accept. Upon closer examination, McCoy states that the generation of male hormones within Decker has increased abnormally.

Kirk is incredulous. "The crippling of my ship . . . the killing of Ibsen, the death of the St. Louis . . . all were for the purpose of sex hormones?"

McCoy theorizes that a way to end the delusions in the commander is to extract hormones from Janice Rand and inject them into him. The action works, and Decker slowly

comes around. The doctor stabilizes Rand and Kelly, and then injects each of them to, hopefully, immunize them to the power of the aliens.

Exploring the laboratory further, McCoy, using his tricorder, discovers that the aliens are hermaphrodites, utilizing humans as catalysts to energize their illusions.

Ronel confronts them with an ancient phaser-like weapon. She is furious that the humans are ruining everything. Kirk responds that they are trying to save the Enterprise, and then questions her about the weapon. Ronel goes on to explain that it is part of the technology left behind by the ancients. It turns out that nearly two billion of her people had been annihilated in a one day war. "Creating was not enough," she says, "they had to dominate . . . Now you know why we cannot let it happen again."

McCoy doesn't see the connection, but Kirk does. Fantasy sex is being used by the aliens to fill a void in their lives, as they placate their aggressions to gain peace. Ronel adds that they are unable to produce the hormones they need and, as a result, their old aggressions are coming back to the surface.

"Learn," exclaims Kirk. "Use your aggressions to find solutions!"

As a last recourse, and choosing to ignore the captain, Ronel prepares to launch a missile to destroy the dilithium they have in hiding. On the Enterprise, Xon calculates the missile's trajectory, and locates the power source they so desperately need. The starship takes the brunt of the missile's force, survives and beams up the dilithium ores. They have 30 seconds before the vessel enters the atmosphere. Needless to say, Enterprise is saved at the last possible instant.

Some time later on the bridge, Xon wonders if Ronel's people will soon destroy themselves in a war. Perhaps, he suggests, a team of Vulcan scientists should be sent to aid them.

"Help them do what – obtain an endless supply of hormones?" Kirk responds. "And how much is enough before the same problem becomes overpowering again?"

* * *

This would have been one of those occasions where they concluded on a somewhat downbeat note, with the possible extinction of an alien race. It is logical and a more realistic conclusion to the story presented.

"Are Unheard Melodies Sweet?" deals much more openly with sex than the original series could have, and emphasizes how an updated version of Star Trek could differ from its source material. The only real complaint is that, in some ways, the story is an amalgamation of several previous episodes, most notably "The Cage", "The Man Trap, "Shore Leave" and "This Side of Paradise." The story also suffers from the imminent destruction of the Enterprise standard cliché also found in "The Savage Syndrome" and several others.

Gene Roddenberry was rather pleased with the script, and, while in the midst of preparing for Star Trek: The Motion Picture, shot a memo off to writer Worley Thorne on February 21, 1978, noting, "This is definitely a good beginning toward the kind of episode we want . . . you are on the right track." From there he listed seven pages worth of notes concerning small plot points, character discrepancies and suggestions concerning certain passages of dialogue. He concluded, "I am looking forward to an excellent second draft."

The script began as a treatment entitled "Home," which is dated September 13, 1977. The basic premise was the same, but the specifics in some cases were quite different. For example, Decker, once on the planet's surface, finds himself in a fantasy where he is reconciled with his father before his death. (Note: In this treatment, his father was not Commodore Decker from "The Doomsday Machine".) Uhura, too, finds herself back on Earth, once more trying to follow the career in music she pursued before signing up with Starfleet.

Kirk pretty much stays on the bridge, while others head the landing parties. In fact, it is Xon who beams down and saves the day. Also, the Grokhoors are absorbing antibodies rather than hormones in order to correct physical imperfections brought about by continued exposure to Capellan Spores. Thankfully much of this was changed, although it is commendable that Worley Thorne attempted to give the new crewmembers lead status.

STAR TREK: THE NEXT GENERATION
(1987–1994)

"THE BONDING"
WRITTEN BY LEE MADDUX

Enterprise is holding its position at the mid-point of two planets belonging to the Federation, Picard having been instructed to study the current territorial dispute between the worlds, and arbitrate some sort of treaty. On the bridge, the captain, Riker, Worf and Data are studying space maps of the area in question, and it seems as though the Klingon is distracted by something. It is Picard's serious recommendation that Worf keep his mind on the situation at hand. Data passes a look conveying concern.

As the author details it, the following events were designed the way they are so that they could show the ship's computer at work in its various functions, including the preparation of food, crewmembers' use of the turbolift and the mending of a torn uniform.

Back on the bridge, Picard is a bit startled to be contacted by Starfleet, which orders him to put his current mission on hold so that he can investigate civil disturbances on Omega Croton IV. The starship is to shuttle "refugees to a medical base." This is also accepted by the other planets involved in Enterprise's original mission.

As the Enterprise proceeds to Croton, Data informs the bridge crew that the planet is ruled by a humanoid race, who "function on a superior form of artificial intelligence." Apparently these people have amazing telekinetic abilities, and they have spent the past few centuries supplying their Subjects with just about anything they desire. The reason for

this sudden revolt on the part of the Subjects is a bit of a mystery. Once they reach their destination, however, the refugees are beamed aboard [which makes one ask why Starfleet's orders were that they be "shuttled" to a medical base]. An older woman manages to move away from the crowd and enters an empty room, where a Croton infant is placed in an air duct. Then she actually wills the life out of her body, and collapses to the deck. Meanwhile, the male child in the duct "gurgles" and, as though in response, the computer emits a gust of warm air, which is followed by a "web-like diaper" which covers the child's bottom.

Act One: We're told that the mission has been accomplished, and the refugees transported to the medical base. The Enterprise begins journeying back to their original site. Geordi punches in the coordinates and he, too, realizes that something is wrong with Worf. The Klingon just doesn't seem to be himself. Back in the air duct, the infant has willed a "clear bladder filled with baby formula" to approach him, and he begins to feed from it. At that moment, an engineer hears the sound of a soft burp and investigates the situation. He enters the room and finds the woman's dead body.

Later, Doctor Beverly Crusher studies the corpse in sickbay, and tells Picard that this woman was actually a Croton who had somehow altered her skin-color blue so that she could pass for a Subject, and had actually managed to will herself to die. The captain wants her to perform an autopsy. Meanwhile, in the bridge lounge, Deanna Troi is discussing Worf's behavior with Data, suggesting

that whatever is troubling the Klingon is of a deeply personal nature. Data concurs, offering to study his behavioral patterns.

Upon returning to the bridge, Picard informs Starfleet of the woman's death, stating that for the sake of diplomacy, they will discuss what will happen to the body *after* an autopsy has been conducted. Then, Worf warns that an ion storm is approaching the ship, but the captain is confident that the Enterprise's shields will have no trouble withstanding such a storm. We intercut to the air duct, where the turbulence striking the ship has caused the infant to start crying, and then we go back to the bridge. Abruptly, the starship steers clear of the storm, which infuriates Picard. He wants to know why Geordi went against his orders and changed course. Geordi quickly responds that he had nothing to do with it, and that the ship's computer actually took control of navigation. Turning his anger to the computer, then, Picard wants an explanation. Shockingly, it points out that its "child" might have been injured had the Enterprise tried to ride through the storm. We cut back down to the air duct, where the child, which has already grown quite a bit, is sound asleep.

Act Two begins with Picard wanting to know where this mysterious child is. The computer's maternal instinct(?) takes over, and it wants to inform the infant that the humans on board mean it no harm. Simultaneously, Troi and Data have discovered the computer has been shipping supplies to the little boy, but no sooner have they made this discovery than it tells them the child's location. Picard tells Riker to have the Enterprise return to the survey site, as he leaves the bridge. Tasha Yar, in the meantime, removes the boy from the air duct and hands him over to an awaiting medical officer, who will take it to the pediatric center. The youth has now aged to approximately eighteen months.

As Crusher and Picard approach sickbay, she states that her autopsy was able to show the deceased woman's final hours of visual imagery, because, as the author explains it, "it's now possible to view what the woman saw in the last hours of her life."

Bridge: Data's viewscreen flashes with the words "Abnormal Behavior in Klingons," but unfortunately Worf has seen this as well, and his reaction cuts deeply into the android. Back in sickbay, Picard and Crusher view the dead woman's final hours, and see her at a Croton temple where she is handed an infant. Then the temple explodes, and she hides the child beneath her clothing and makes a desperate run for it. Further information obtained indicates that this child is the ruler of Croton. They're interrupted by a communiqué stating that *something* has happened to the child. Picard and Riker proceed to the pediatric center, where they discover that the boy is now ten years old, extremely intelligent and articulate. He states that his name is Pattrue, and verifies their theory that he is the ruler of Croton. According to the treatment, this boy possesses computerized intelligence and in an emotionless tone asks to be granted political asylum; to remain on board the Enterprise until the situation on his home planet has settled down. Picard says he will consider his request.

Upon returning to the bridge, the captain, Riker and Data try to determine what should be done with Pattrue. Geordi interrupts, stating that something is beginning to absorb massive amounts of data from the ship's computer.

Act Three picks up the action on the bridge, with the crew realizing that information is being "siphoned off" at an incredible rate of speed. Picard deduces that whoever is responsible is on board, and he gives both Riker and Tasha the assignment of trying to find out exactly who or what it might be. The search begins and ultimately concludes in a utility corridor, where Pattrue is floating in mid-air, and in the midst of absorbing the information from the ship's computer.

Bridge: Riker orders the computer to cease giving out information to the child, but the device refuses, explaining that for the boy to be able to complete his mission, he must have the information stored in the ship's memory banks. As the treatment notes, "For centuries the Crotons have been isolationists. The caliber of their life style and their sense of security has been slowly deteriorating due to the lack of new input. Hence, the revolution by the Subjects." At this point, Data makes it clear that the information from the computer is merely being shared with the boy, and not erased from the memory banks. Picard begins wondering if this action is in violation of the Prime Directive, and he contacts Starfleet for an answer. The response comes soon enough, with that organization stating that the Subjects have agreed to settle their disagreement with Croton, provided Pattrue is returned to their world [Now this makes no sense. How could Starfleet have an answer for Picard, when the captain himself is right there in the midst of the situation? It probably would have been more effective to have the captain decided for himself whether or not they were breaking the Prime Directive, and then taking the appropriate action. In this case, he comes across as little more than a "momma's boy," finding it necessary to contact his parent organization before making a decision]. The captain is told to return the boy to his home world, but *after* the survey mission is done – again, seemingly another mistake in logic.

Eventually, Wesley Crusher befriends Pattrue and takes him on a tour of the Enterprise [which you just *know* is going to lead to trouble in one form or another], moving through engineering, where feelings of frustration are explained to Pattrue, and then to sickbay, where the boy views parents expressing joy and love to their child. He tries to understand the feeling, but finds it difficult to do so, although he does smile at the family as they depart.

Act Four: the Enterprise has reached the final phase of their survey, while at the same time Data has discovered what the problem is with Worf: every two decades Klingons re-enact their "initiation rite into warriorship." Worf believes that, as the only representative of his race, there will be no way for him to partake in such a ceremony. Worf is sent to his quarters, and no sooner has he gone than Picard states his willingness to allow Geordi, Tasha and Data to partake in a "surprise ceremony." He does, however, issue warnings of safety, given the nature of Klingon ceremonies.

To be honest, this whole sequence of events really does seem out of place. Why, in the middle of all that's going on, would anyone worry about such a ceremony? Additionally, can we honestly believe that this highly trained Starfleet officer is going to worry so much about a ceremony that he will allow himself to be distracted and perhaps accidentally endanger the ship? Also, the whole idea of "every twenty years, Klingons ..." sounds a bit too much like Spock's "every seven years Vulcans must ..." from the "Amok Time" episode of the original *Star Trek*.

Elsewhere, Wes and Pattrue, who is showing more emotion, continue their exploration of the ship, coming across an embracing couple, and giggling in response. Meanwhile, Data, Geordi and Tasha are preparing for the ceremony by getting their hands on devices known as "pain sticks." Data is admittedly concerned, drawing the analogy that staging an attack against a Klingon might be akin to standing in front of a photon torpedo which is about to be launched.

A little while later, Wes and Pattrue make their way by Worf's quarters, where they hear screams coming from within. They investigate, only to find that Worf is being beaten down by his three opponents. Pattrue moves in to help the Klingon, but Wes stops him, explaining that this moment of humiliation is one which is celebrated by the Klingons [though one has got to ask why]. The author notes that, "As the beaten Worf gasps for air, he tearfully thanks Data, Geordi and Tasha. Because he was humiliated by friends, it was the finest humiliation he'd ever experienced.

Great. Super. Wonderful. What the hell is this all about? It seems extremely hard to believe that the Klingons would get off on having themselves humiliated in a ceremony. This just seems to be extraneous material added to the story that really doesn't serve much purpose.

As the ceremony comes to a close, Pattrue is truly excited at having witnessed such a demonstration of friendship on the part of Worf's crewmates. He adds that on his homeworld, there is nothing that compares to what he's just seen. Such expressions of sentiment would not be logical or condoned. Back on the bridge, the course is laid in for Croton just as the two boys enter. Pat-

true startles everyone by stating that he doesn't wish to return to his home world because he cannot live in a society which does not express true feelings.

Act Five: Picard is meeting with Beverly and Wes in the ready room, where the boy states that by exposing Pattrue to emotion, he has moved him from a purely logical view of the universe. Unfortunately, if Pattrue doesn't return, the situation could become extremely critical. It is the captain's opinion that at this point Wes may be the only one able to change the boy's mind. He goes to see Pattrue in sickbay, and tries to convince him, but he doesn't want to hear any of it. There is absolutely no way that he could convince his entire society that there is a place for emotions. It is Pattrue's opinion that the people of Croton will work out their own problems. The two boys are then ordered to the bridge, where they learn that the treaty has been broken on Croton, and there is a battle taking place near the Royal Palace. Pattrue, now equipped with his new-found emotions, is extremely touched by the carnage he is witness to, and realizes that there is no choice but to return to his people. Will they accept him, though, after he has broken Croton law regarding emotion? Picard implies that there might be a "loophole" to the law, and the boy, beginning to levitate, mentally moves his mind through every volume on Croton's surface, and eventually comes to the conclusion that since the planet's laws had been

based on a caste system, by making all beings equal, those laws would become null and void. Perhaps, he feels, a feeling of true brotherhood would follow, where everyone would learn to experience the magic of emotions.

Pattrue goes to the transporter room, bids Wes farewell, and beams down to the planet's surface, with the ship's computer telling him that he should "Go in peace."

* * *

"The Bonding" doesn't really work, and one can see why it wasn't taken any further than the outline stage. While the basic idea of Pattrue is an intriguing one, the story doesn't make the best use of him that it could. Besides, the idea of a cold, and logical being seeking and ultimately discovering the value of emotions is an old one in the *Star Trek* mythos, and will never be done better than in the form of Mr. Spock. Interestingly, the image of the old woman smuggling the infant on board the Enterprise so that he will, in effect, lead his people to freedom, is very much like that of Moses in *The Ten Commandments.* Also, the idea of an infant rapidly aging to a child would eventually be used in the second season premiere episode of *The Next Generation,* "The Child," which, in turn, was based on the script of the same name written for the proposed *Star Trek II* series of the mid 1970s. The ceremony involving Worf was altered somewhat and utilized in the episode, "The Icarus Factor."

"TERMINUS"
Written by Philip and Eugene Price
Revised by Robert Lewin and Dorothy Fontana

Captain Picard has been instructed to deliver supplies to Bynax II, which is being considered as a Starbase terminal. The mission is under the command of old friend Ty Norsen. Unfortunately, what started as a unextraordinary assignment, turns extremely serious as the Enterprise receives a distress signal from Norsen, who claims that Bynax II is in extreme danger. Nothing else is stated in the announcement.

After the vessel's speed has been increased, scanners pick up an unidentifiable object which is approaching them. Further study reveals it to be mechanical in nature, with its speed increasing. Enterprise shields are raised, as are those on the object. Magnifying the image on the main viewscreen, the crew sees that this object is "unique, mysterious – and ominous." It's obvious that everyone is growing concerned over this potential danger, with the exception of Data, who actually starts to smile, which, in turn, becomes a laugh, as Data states that the object means them no harm. Picard, naturally enough, is concerned by this unusual behavior, asking Data why this is the first time that he's ever laughed. The android doesn't have an answer, but he keeps on smiling. The object passes the Enterprise, and continues traveling beyond the ship.

Act One: Concern has grown greatly on the Enterprise, with the fear being that this alien device is en route to Bynax II, but projections reveal that this does not seem to be the case. The ship finally reaches the planet, and the crew is stunned to learn that there are no life forms evident on the surface. An Away Team is sent down to investigate, and, still being unable to locate anyone, Riker grows concerned that this, combined with the distress signal the Enterprise had received earlier, indicates that something terrible must have happened. Data disagrees, actually referring to the commander as an alarmist, which turns out to be an accurate description when, with Geordi's aid, they learn that the people are living safely underground, although they are angry that Norsen had moved them there in the first place. Riker informs the commodore that they found nothing threatening on the surface, and everyone moves back up there.

Riker tries to figure out what's going on, but Norsen is extremely uncooperative, even when Picard tries to get some answers. What the captain really wants to know is how Norsen had been able to send a distress signal *before* there had been any danger. Also on his mind is Data's previous strange behavior, and his lack of knowledge of why he was laughing. On the surface, Geordi's special vision detects waves of energy, but Norsen refuses to allow him to investigate. Back on the Enterprise, the alien object has appeared again. It passes the starship and begins scanning the planet. Picard contacts Riker to pass on the information. Norsen demands protection, which the starship will naturally supply, but then the object vanishes. Picard and Troi begin contemplating the possibility that Norsen is being controlled by an outside intelligence.

Act Two: Data and Geordi begin tracking the energy waves, and are eventually led to an object which is an exact replica of the one that has been spotted by the Enterprise. Norsen, his people and the rest of the Away Team join them, and stare at this object which they had never seen on the surface before. After tricorder readings are taken, Riker wants to drill into it so that they can obtain a sample of the material for study. Both Data and Norsen voice their objections, but Riker essentially overrules them on this. The drilling is started, but everyone is thrown back by the release of energy from the object. They move into hiding.

The space version of the object reappears, and begins to "gamma-ray" the surface, killing the people who had remained. The only survivor is someone who was feverish beforehand. This man is beamed to sickbay, with Data taken up to the Enterprise because of the way he has been acting as of late. Apparently he is in the midst of some sort of malfunction. Once on the ship, he meets with Picard, admitting that he himself doesn't really understand his behavior. He asks for, and is granted, permission to return to quarters so that he can provide himself with a self-check of his systems. Once there, the android makes a valiant attempt to reprogram himself to weed out anything negative in his system, but is surprised to find that he cannot. Wesley arrives, tells his friend that the best thing for him to do is to go speak to Beverly, but Data refuses, stating that the best thing he could do is to stay by himself for the moment. Ultimately Data comes to the conclusion that he can no longer serve a useful purpose on the Enterprise, and therefore he must end his own existence before he brings harm to anyone else.

Act Three: Picard, finding himself torn between events on the planet and the situation with Data, has Geordi beamed back aboard so that he can deal with the android. Once there, he does his best, but his pleas fall on deaf ears. Data feels responsible for the deaths of those people on the surface, and nothing can change that, not even the pleas of Beverly and Wesley. Seeing no alternative, Picard restricts Data to quarters, and assigns a team of security guards to make sure he doesn't do something drastic. Data points out that the guards are useless, as he can simply will himself to die. Bearing this in mind, Picard tells the guards that he wants to be notified if Data even appears to be doing something he shouldn't be doing, right down to closing his eyes. Outside of this, he really doesn't know what else he can do.

Meanwhile, Norsen finally agrees to beam up to the bridge to discuss the situation with Picard. The captain comes right out and asks the other man if he has some kind of "unholy alliance with this killer object." Furious, Norsen replies in the negative, merely pointing out that his prediction of danger has turned out correct, although he never explains just how he was able to come to this conclusion.

In his quarters, Data has closed his eyes and seems to be completely "dead," but Wesley, who has come to keep him company, begs the android not to die, expressing his love [gag city — imagine how this would have played on film]. Data manages to open his eyes, and tells the boy that he should not be upset. There is one thing, however, that can be done for him. A favor: he would like to see the stars one more time, and asks that Wesley take him to the observation lounge. Naturally he agrees, telling the guards that Data is recovering. The guard accepts this, stating that he will join them in the lounge.

One question: shouldn't somebody notify that captain of this situation? When Picard confines somebody to quarters, one would think that that person would stay there, and the guards would ensure this until the *captain* says otherwise.

Back on the planet, Riker is stunned to find Data there, knowing full well that the android is supposed to be on the Enterprise. He contacts Picard, who states that Data is supposed to be in his quarters. A search begins for the android, who, the captain discovers, is missing.

Act Four: Wesley and the guard explain to Picard that Data managed to elude them as they were enroute to the lounge. Opening a channel with the transporter room, the captain

is surprised to be told that no one has beamed down. Confused, Picard nonetheless has Riker put the Data on the surface in restraints and beamed back aboard the ship. Still on the bridge, he turns his attention back to Norsen, trying to make some sense of this bizarre situation. There are no answers coming, and their conversation is interrupted, again, by the announcement that Data has been beamed up. Picard orders him confined to quarters.

Elsewhere on the Enterprise, Data awakens, his audio-sensors picking up the announcement that he had been beamed up and confined to quarters. He weakly makes his way there, telling the surprised guard that he managed to escape. Entering, Data "finds himself face to face with another Data, almost, but not exactly, like himself."

Act Five: After a conversation between themselves, the two Datas are brought to the bridge, where, at last, the mystery of the planet begins to be revealed. What they discover is that the object on the planet's surface is an exact duplicate of the device which had created Data on his native world, and has actually played a large hand in making Bynax II a habitable planet. Apparently there are many of these devices located at strategic points throughout the universe, all doing their best to help humanity, who they admire very much. The basis of these feelings come from the Earth-Asian planet where Data was found. One of these devices had been destroyed by humans on a faraway planet, and, angry, a duplicate was sent out to hunt the people responsible down and extract revenge. Unfortunately something went wrong with the programming, and that particular object just continued in its mission to wipe out human life forms. The communicating ability of the objects reached the one stationed on Bynax II, and the only way for it to communicate the threat was to "influence" Norsen's thought patterns

by giving him the image of the imminent destruction, thus allowing the man to lead the colony underground before the object arrived to unleash its wrath. When the message wasn't clear enough, it created a copy of Data, the only other machine-image it was aware of, and this version (referred to in the outline as Data II) was given the task of warning everyone that the device was heading their way.

At that moment, the object returns. Data II suggests that Picard beam the Away Team and the others underground, because the object tracks its victims down by "sensing respiration and body temperature, which is why the human with a fever was passed over by the death beams. The bridge team realizes that it must somehow come up with a way to draw the object back so that they can destroy it. Wesley, being the boy genius that he is, devises "several 98.6-degree objects, within a carbon dioxide 'shell' that will do the trick." While the captain feels that they should beam the objects down to the surface, Data II interjects that he was created to follow through on such an action. Picard considers this for a moment, yields to the logic and agrees. Shortly thereafter, Data II beams down with the boy's creations, which do, indeed, lure the alien object out into the open and it bombards the surface, as well as Data II, with gamma-rays. Taking advantage of the opportunity, Enterprise opens fire with photon torpedoes, which destroy it instantly.

Later, the Away Team, which was safely underground with Norsen's people, is beamed aboard, with Norsen returning to the planet, after thanking Picard for all his help. Before the Enterprise breaks orbit, the image of Norsen and Data II fill the viewscreen, assuring everyone that they will continue their work on Bynax II.

* * *

"Terminus" is only a so-so offering,

neither being overly terrible nor overly good. Bearing in mind that this is only an outline, one can assume that the story would have been more refined and fleshed out had the pro- duction team decided to take it further. Certain elements of this story would find their way into other epi- sodes. Most notably, the duplicate Data idea would reappear in "Data- lore," and the alien-object element which reproduces itself and threatens a planet as well as the Enterprise would resurface in "Arsenal of Free- dom."

"THE NEUTRAL ZONE"
Written by Greg Strangis

Enterprise is awaiting the arrival of Commander Billings, a chief of security from Starfleet Command. Naturally, Tasha Yar is particularly concerned about this visit, as security is her domain. Riker would love to know the purpose of this visit, as would Picard. The captain turns to Data for information on Billings, but, surprisingly, Tasha has more to offer than the android does. According to the treatment, her eyes are sparkling and it rapidly becomes apparent that there's more to what she knows than just trivia. Billings "wrote the book" on security, and was once an instructor at the Academy who was highly respected by students and peers alike. But, for the most part, the last few years have become a mystery as to Billings' life. He has more or less avoided the public spotlight.

Later, the Enterprise finally meets with the starcruiser Washington, but, for some reason, Billings (sounding very much like Bones McCoy) refuses to beam over, choosing, instead, to utilize a shuttlecraft. This is done, and as the doors open, the crew is a bit stunned to see Billings float out of the shuttle in what is deemed the 24th Century equivalent of a wheelchair. He is "severely disabled."

Act One: Despite the fact that he is crippled at the age of 40, Billings seems to be very lively. Tasha asks if he will need any specific accommodations to help him physically, to which he replies in the negative. The treatment also makes note of the fact that Wes hovers around the chair, fascinated by this apparently new aspect of technology. The boy tries to question him about the workings of the wheelchair, but Billings tersely turns to Picard, wondering why a youth has access to the bridge of the Enterprise. Evading the question

(although Picard probably should have made some reference to the boy's natural abilities), the captain asks for an explanation of the nature of this mission. Billings is not yet ready to answer, stating that all things will become clear in time. For the moment, he would like to take the "scenic-route" of the ship so that he may best determine the status of ship security. Tasha leads him off the bridge. While Riker, Geordi, Worf and Picard discuss Billings, they manage to determine that their current heading will lead the Enterprise to the Neutral Zone, which serves as the territorial bounds between Federation space and that of the Romulans. While the captain is obviously concerned, it's just as obvious that Worf would love nothing more than a good tangle with the Romulans.

Billings and Tasha, meanwhile, have arrived on the battle bridge, where he asks her particular questions regarding security, and she seems to respond appropriately. He turns the conversation to the Romulans, wanting to determine if anyone on board has had any contact with that race. Before beginning her computer check, she asks if the failed Earth colony known as Davana VII (which is the world that she was rescued from) means anything to him, but his blunt response is that Davana VII was a long time ago in history, and bears no meaning on the mission at hand. Tasha is hurt by this, but says nothing.

In sickbay, Data is working with Beverly Crusher on an experiment pertaining to organ regeneration. As has happened often in the past, Beverly is puzzled by the android's physiology, stating that what her medical instruments state cannot possibly be true. Being as logical as ever, Data points out the fact that he exists is the one thing that does matter in this case. How he exists does not. On the bridge, Tasha and Billings have returned with a breakdown of people who will have to be dropped off at the next starbase they come across for the duration of this mission. Worf's

name is on the list, and such a suggestion infuriates Picard. Worf protests, but the captain silences him, turning to Billings and stating, quite firmly, that the crew of the Enterprise was hand-picked and they are beyond reproach. He will not transfer any of his people off, but to satisfy Billings, he will temporarily reassign Worf as Wes' tutor. While not completely happy with this decision, Billings accepts it, feeling that two security risks will be removed from the bridge. Then, Picard leads Billings into the ready room, demanding to know what in hell is going on. Finally, the man gives a response, stating that Enterprise will serve as the base for an extremely important trade conference which will be the first to include the Romulan Empire. *But* there are factions among that race who would rather such an agreement not be reached. For this reason, the security of the starship is of paramount importance. Worf, he points out, undoubtedly has a cultural hatred towards the Romulans, and he feels that for security purposes the Klingon should be removed from the mix. Picard bluntly points out that he himself is not very fond of the Romulans, and had even engaged a pair of Bird of Prey in battle several years earlier. Billings is aware of this, stating that that battle forced the Romulans to look at the captain with honor, which is why they did not ask for the Enterprise as a location for the trade conference — they merely wanted Picard to be there.

Act Two: Visiting Beverly in sickbay, Tasha asks for advice on how she can let someone know that she admires him on more than a professional level. It is the doctor's recommendation that she use the direct approach. Later, in the turbolift, Beverly runs into Billings, wanting to know why the man has refused her requests for a complete physical. He offers some feeble excuses, and she turns the request into an order.

Billings comes to see Tasha in security to check out how things are progressing. Tasha notes that he is the one responsible for getting her involved in Starfleet and security in the first place. Billings led the Starfleet security forces who rescued her and others from Davana VII, and she feels that she owes him a debt that can never be repaid. Surprisingly, Billings virtually ignores what she's said, pointing out that that mission was nothing out of the ordinary. He then, rudely, turns the conversation back to Enterprise security, chastising her for what he's seen so far. Things have to be tightened up on the ship. He departs, leaving a stunned and hurt Tasha behind. Moments later, Geordi and Wes enter, angered by the fact they've been restricted from certain areas of the ship. Quietly, Tasha provides the explanation given to her, which does not sit well with them. As the treatment notes, "Efficiency as well as harmony are beginning to suffer."

In sickbay, Beverly is in the midst of examining Billings, having come to the conclusion that he sustained injuries in the midst of some sort of heroism. Billings doesn't wish to talk about it. Changing the subject slightly, she points out that she and Data have been performing experiments, which *could* take nutrients from the android's spinal cord, inject them into Billings, which might then, in turn, possibly result in the regeneration of his "damaged nerve ends." He refuses, stating that this is just another attempt which would raise his hopes and then destroy them when the experiment failed. He has finally come to grips with his situation, and learned to accept it. As the man leaves, Wes runs into him, stating that he if could have access to restricted materials located in restricted areas, he believes he could enhance Billings' wheelchair. The man snaps that he doesn't need anyone's help, and he moves away from the boy.

The Enterprise arrives at the Neutral Zone and word comes in that a Romulan ship is approaching. The ship is put on yellow alert, with Billings

being requested to come to the bridge. The Romulan ship is hailed, to which it responds as Billings enters the bridge. A security officer from that vessel beams aboard, with Riker, Tasha and Data going to the transporter room to meet him. There, Sub-Commander Gar appears on the platform, immediately commenting on how primitive the Enterprise transporter is. He is escorted out of the room and into a corridor, where Worf and Wes stand. The Klingon and Romulan exchange scowls, with Worf muttering a racial remark as the group passes.

Moments later, in the captain's ready room, Gar explains that despite popular belief, the Empire has decided to follow through with this trade conference, although the conclusion will undoubtedly be disastrous. Gar's assignment is to make sure that the Romulan delegates will be safe on board the Enterprise. Picard is not happy with Gar's presence, particularly when it's been noted that he would probably love to see these talks fail.

Act Three: In sickbay, Beverly is asking Tasha if she thinks there might be a way to convince Billings to go through with the experiments. Tasha, still pained by her previous encounter with the man, doesn't have an answer, although she will look over the material pertaining to the experiment. Elsewhere, Gar is being given a tour of the Enterprise, to satisfy his concern over ship security.

In the ship's library, Worf is delivering a lecture on Klingon history — which comes across as little more than a list of battles, but Wes is fascinated by what his tutor has to say. He also discusses a Klingon-Romulan battle, where the former proved victorious, but Gar, who has just entered the area, states that Klingon history is quite different from the way things really happened (according to the Romulans, that is). They exchange insults, the "session" concluding with Worf noting that Klingons must be superior, as the Romulans copied their battleship

design from them. This seems to quiet Gar down a bit, as he turns his attention back to security. He wants to finish the inspection alone, to which Riker objects, but Billings notes that if the Enterprise is truly secure, then there is nothing to fear. The commander contacts Picard, while Gar makes another insult against Worf before leaving the area.

"How can someone look so much like a Vulcan, yet act like such a moron?" Worf muses (great line).

Wes and Worf go to the transporter room, but are told by the computer that their access is denied. Wes confidently pulls out a tape recorder, and plays the captain's voice rescinding the restriction of this area. The doors open, and they enter.

This is a ploy Wes used in "The Naked Now," where he utilized the voice of the captain to get access to the engineering section. While some people may look at this as the repetition of an idea, it can also be construed as a bit of continuity within the series.

Wes, operating the console, beams Worf into a storage room, telling the Klingon that in five minutes he will automatically beam back. Moments later, he reappears with a variety of items.

While Gar continues his inspection, Tasha talks with Billings, with the man deducing that Doctor Crusher has requested her to speak with him. From there he lets her know that he is aware of her records, and had expected her gratitude to him to be distorted by his handicap into something she *imagined* to be romantic. Again, she's hurt by this, but he tells her to deal with "life's painful realities rather than dwelling on romantic memories." If nothing else, Tasha realizes that Billings has truly come to grips with the fact that he will remain crippled for the rest of his life.

Gar returns to the bridge just as the vessel containing the trade delegates nears the Enterprise. He approves security measures and tells them to beam the delegates, beginning with the Romulans, aboard. Riker, Data and Tasha are awaiting their arrival in the transporter room. In mid-operation, there are a series of warning klaxons and flashing lights, with the fear being that the expected malfunction will beam the Romulans in the middle of space. Panic on the bridge, with Gar reacting angrily to Picard. Geordi crossfeeds an alternate power source into the transporter power line, hoping that it will be enough. This move, combined with Riker and Data's efforts, manages to get the Romulans back to their own ship, the delegates wanting to know what happened. Picard, too, would like an answer. In the transporter room, Data removes a device from the console, noting that it was sabotage which almost cost the lives of the delegates.

Act Four: Wesley tells Picard that he had used the transporter controls, although it was done for an innocent enough reason. In the ready room, Worf explains exactly what he and Wes had done, confessing that he's guilty for entering a restricted area, while simultaneously stating that neither of them were involved in sabotaging the device. Gar once again reinforces how bad this idea of a trade agreement was in the first place. Picard tells Tasha to take Worf into custody until the situation can be investigated in more detail. When the two are alone, Worf proclaims his innocence, stating that if he was really going to do harm to a Romulan, he would have done it face-to-face, which is the way Klingons handle things. She is moved by his statements. In the ready room, Gar demands to be sent back to his ship, which Picard will happily comply with once the transporter has been repaired. Billings is angry, pointing out that he was the one who wanted Worf taken off the ship in the first place. How will the Romulans react to what has happened? Tasha contacts the ready room, requesting that everyone

be ready for an image to appear on the main viewscreen.

They do so, and Tasha explains that she had kept a record of all authorized areas as well as unauthorized personnel – which infuriates Billings, because he wasn't told (but why should she have after his reaction to everything else Tasha had to offer?) and the computer tape shows Worf and Wes entering the transporter room. Later, the image reveals Gar entering the room as well. She calls up another image, and everyone sees Gar opening a panel and inserting a foreign object. Tasha has the image frozen.

Furious, Picard turns his attention to Gar, who "offers the Romulan equivalent of a shrug." While he admits his guilt, he strikes it up to the general feeling that détente between their two people would be a mistake. Gar, as he explains it, merely helped to speed up the natural state of things. As things develop, and with the guilty party under arrest, the trade conference continues and everyone – except Billings – seems to come out on top. Later, Billings apologizes to Tasha, but she is rather brusque with him, leaving the security office. Wes enters with schematics as well as a scale model of his idea for the man's new wheelchair. Unfortunately Billings' mind is preoccupied with Tasha.

Act Five: As the Enterprise and Romulan vessels move away from each other, Picard's log states that the trade conference was a success, and that if he's lucky, the Romulans will allow Gar to take his own life, which is that race's form of death with honor.

Later, Billings is with Beverly, studying Wes' model and voicing his approval of it. If it's alright with the boy, he would like to give the design to Federation researchers so that it can be developed for practical use throughout their territory. Beverly thinks this would be fine, but why not allow the boy to develop the first unit for him? Billings coyly notes that he

had hoped he wouldn't need it. Shortly thereafter, both Billings and Data are on adjoining tables in sickbay, and Beverly conducts the operation discussed earlier.

Still later, on the main bridge, everyone is at their post, with Enterprise en route to meet with Billings' ship. Suddenly, there's another emergency. Enterprise has to deliver dilithium crystals to an "out-of-the-way" starbase, and the new course is laid in. At that moment, Billings *walks* in, a cane in his hand. Everyone is delighted. Billings, who is pleased beyond words, approaches Tasha and asks if she could possibly join him for dinner, as he has learned that solitude in large degrees can have nothing but a damaging effect on a person's humanity. Without responding to the man, Tasha receives permission from Picard to leave the bridge. Billings offers her his arm, and the two of them approach the turbo lift, with Picard making note of the fact that they will have to detour to Gorn space for a short while. Billings replies that there is no rush, as he and Tasha enter the turbolift.

* * *

Despite the fact that the very basic elements of this story reminds one of the original show's "Journey to Babel," "The Neutral Zone" would have made a wonderful episode of *The Next Generation*. There's plenty of mystery, a great deal of characterization and actually some snap in the form of internal conflict of the main players. Worf, in particular, is handled nicely. His racial intolerance of the Romulans would be brought to life – in full glory – in season three's "The Enemy." Elements of this plot, from a possible détente between the Federation and one of its enemies to a member of the "other side" attempting to sabotage negotiations, would come up again – surprisingly enough – in the motion picture, *Star Trek VI: The Undiscovered Country*.

"SOMEWHEN"
Written by Vanna Bonta

Enterprise is responding to a distress signal (there always seems to be *somebody* in distress) from a passenger ship called the Pleides. Their heading is the Docleic Triad, which is essentially an outer-space equivalent of the Bermuda Triangle, with a wide variety of ships having been lost there over the years. Data explains that scanners indicate an ion storm had recently passed through that area of space. Past studies have revealed that the effect of such storms is to create "an electromagnetic 'waterspout' effect," which has been powerful enough to destroy vessels. The sensors indicate a phenomenon termed spheres within spheres, which are a series of "rings" made of energy. The situation is a dangerous one, but should they proceed? As the distress signal continues from the Pleides, the captain realizes that there is no choice. They must go on with their mission. The ship is put on full alert, while Tasha realizes that holodeck 1B is being utilized without authorization, but there is no one there. Worf is sent to investigate. Finding nothing out of the ordinary, he contacts her, states that the unit is not being used, and walks away. Then we "see a glow of light from the holodeck," and the image within shows Tasha adorned in a futuristic bathing suit, in the midst of a wild beach party.

Act One: As the Enterprise enters the Docleic Triad, Picard voices his determination to save the Pleides' crew of over one thousand people, and notes that many ships have survived passage through the Triad, although others have not. We also learn that he is being driven in part, by the fact that the next day is the anniversary of Jack Crusher's death, but how much can he risk?

While the Jack Crusher connection is an interesting one, we're never really given the reason for its presence here. What does the Pleides have to do with his death? From what we know, the Stargazer (the vessel on which Picard and Crusher had served together) did not enter the Triad, so it's difficult to discern the connection between the two.

Meanwhile, in her quarters, Beverly, too, is reflecting on Jack's death, staring at a holographic photo of the man, and feeling sorry that Wesley, who is nearby reading a textbook, never really got to know his father. Back on the bridge, and after the Enterprise has entered the first ring, Geordi stuns everyone by saying he's picking up readings for the U.S.S. Orion, which was a starship that vanished in the Triad a decade earlier. The ship is just hovering ahead of them, covered in a green glow. Communication attempts prove fruitless, as does the use of the tractor beam. It's as though the Orion isn't really there. Then, Enterprise is set aglow with the green light, but Picard nonetheless orders the ship onwards.

While Data and Geordi sit at their usual positions, a young, and beautiful, ensign approaches, asking Data to sign a report. Surprisingly, neither have ever seen her before, which is particularly strange in Data's case, as his computer memory recognizes every member of the Enterprise crew. She reminds Geordi of someone he had been attracted to at the Academy, but things never worked out.

As Enterprise broaches the next ring, while in her quarters Beverly is in the midst of eating a meal alone. A male voice responds that he has just the right wine to go along with it. Beverly looks up, to see Jack Crusher sitting across from her.

Act Two: It turns out that Beverly and Jack are in personal quarters, but unlike any found aboard the Enterprise. As Beverly discusses a baby she delivered that day, Jack asks if she's sorry that they never had children of their own. She replies in the negative, pointing out that he and her career are more than enough.

Picard, Riker and Data head for the ready room, with Picard and Riker entering first. Data follows and is surprised to find a bearded Picard talking to his first officer, Jack Crusher. The two men toast their ship, the Stargazer. Data moves back onto the bridge, where everything seems to be the way it should be. As the starship enters the third ring, Geordi spots two other vessels, which Data concludes are the Androcles and the Utoria, both glowing red as the Enterprise itself currently is. A channel is opened to the ready room, and Picard and Riker come back to the bridge in response. Data is, naturally, relieved. They try to raise the two vessels, but are unable to do so and there are no life form readings on either.

Analyzing all available information, Data comes up with a theory in which members of the Enterprise crew are ceasing to exist — at least partially — which is why communication with the other ships has been impossible. Picard is confused, wanting to know what he's talking about. Data responds that time is altering, and if they do not find the Pleides quickly, that ship will undoubtedly be lost. Then the Enterprise passes into the fourth ring, resulting in Picard's disappearing from the bridge. A computer search reveals that the captain is in the science analysis lab, but is unreachable. Annoyed, Riker orders Data to find the captain and bring him back to the bridge. To make matters worse, the signal from the Pleides is beginning to break up.

En route, Data sees Geordi with the ensign we had seen earlier, but he is *not blind*. He makes it to the lab, but when he steps through the door he finds himself in Picard's quarters as seen in "The Battle," the captain holding a brandy glass and once again bearded. Data backs out of the room. Picard steps out a moment later, the beard gone, but still holding the brandy glass. Data, without saying anything else, asks that the captain report to the bridge. He arrives at the exact moment that the Pleides is spotted on the viewscreen. Both that ship and the Enterprise are enveloped in a blue glow. The signal from the ship finally stops. Data steps off the turbo lift, telling them that they must leave this area of space. Picard is adamant that they not desert the people on board that ship, but the android quickly responds that they are not picking up life form readings, which means that they and the Pleides are on different dimensional, or time continuum levels. In addition, the longer they remain, the stronger the chance that they, too, will cease to exist. Things continue to get worse with the announcement that a second ion storm is headed toward them and will arrive in two hours, which might then prevent their ever leaving the Triad.

Act Three: Beverly and Data are trying to detect life forms on the Pleides, but all they're picking is the machinery – no organic life. Data theorizes that machines remain constant, whereas people make different choices, thus altering their lives. Somehow that has come into play in this situation. Moving Beverly is the idea that parallel universes can exist (although *Star Trek* fans have known that since the original show's ''Mirror, Mirror'' episode), and the thought that she might exist somewhere else. Wesley pipes in that ''it's more like *somewhen*.''

Picard gives Riker the helm as he departs the bridge, and a moment later the commander is referred to as captain by Geordi. Somehow time has altered again, and Riker is the captain of the Enterprise. Meanwhile, Data is en route to the bridge when he peers in an open door and sees a beaten and bloodied Tasha Yar coming before a judge on her home world, and being sentenced to die. Realizing that another time line is affecting this one, Data continues, passes the real Tasha and then finds a

third one, who is this time a judge playing God with a prisoner. Realizing that three time lines are coming together, Data hurries to the turbo lift. Another time flash, and we see a married Geordi raising a family, having never joined Starfleet. Elsewhere, Picard enters the observatory lounge, and warmly greets Beverly and Jack Crusher.

Both Data and the real Picard enter the bridge simultaneously, and Riker tells them they must abandon the Pleides immediately, as the second ion storm will definitely strike them if they do not get out of the Triad. After much internal debate, Picard gives the order, but the instruments under Geordi's control do not respond correctly.

Act Four: Moving back in the direction they came is difficult, but made slightly easier by Wesley's suggestion that they use the ships they had spotted earlier as signposts which will eventually lead them out. Troi notes that ''according to quantum physics, thought influences time/space relativity.'' Enterprise passes the Androcles and Utoria. Data says he wants to make one more study of the time alterations throughout the ship, and leaves the bridge. Moving quickly, he discovers that as Enterprise makes her way back, parallel ''worlds'' are beginning to collapse, with things returning to normal. He sees true love between an alternate Riker and Troi reverting back to professionalism, and so on.

Enterprise approaches the first ring as fear of the ion storm grows. Wesley is about to offer his opinion, when he suddenly disappears. Computer search confirms that neither he nor his mother are on board the ship. Troi believes that Beverly wanted her life with Jack so badly, that she undoubtedly ''willed or wished'' herself in a life with him, which would mean that Wesley does not exist. Picard, believing that the boy's suggestion is absolutely vital orders the ship back into the Triad so that the two will once again exist.

Act Five: After quite a bit of searching, they come to the parallel world where Picard, Jack and Beverly are serving on the Stargazer. He must somehow speak to her, even though this Beverly has the parallel knowledge of him, and force her to alter her own reality. He details the events of the real Beverly's life on board the Enterprise. Jack doesn't want to lose her, but she continues to sway back and forth in terms of making a decision. Suddenly Wes appears, then disappears again. ''We love you,'' Picard tells her. Wes appears again, with mother and son locking eyes with each other. Ultimately she chooses her son's reality. Jack disappears just as Wesley materializes completely. Beverly steps into her own time line and the three of them head for the bridge.

Once there, the Enterprise is ordered at maximum speed out of the Triad, which is accomplished thanks to Wesley's offering (although we're never told what it is). With the rear-view screen, the Enterprise crew, now safe once again, stares at the electromagnetic phenomenon of the ion storm they've just avoided.

* * *

''Somewhen'' is just too convoluted to have worked as an episode. There is so much happening, that to cram it all into the forty-odd minutes of an average show could result in nothing more than a cursory treatment of the subject matter. In addition, we've already seen brief moments of fantasy brought to life in several episodes, most notably ''Shore Leave'' on the old show, and ''Where None Have Gone Before'' on the new. In fact, there are even elements of ''City on the Edge of Forever,'' what with Beverly having to choose between one life or another – in effect, deciding whether her son or her husband should die. While this was a valiant attempt by the writer, it's probably just as well that it didn't make it to the air.

"THE IMMUNITY SYNDROME"
Written by J D Kurtz

The S.S. Beagle is in its death throes, the captain of the vessel stating as much in his log, pointing out that death is their only hope for freedom. He orders the ship's hatches to be blown, and from outside the craft we see every hatch explode out, taking the atmosphere from within with them. As the author notes, "the S.S . . . Beagle dies, preserved for all eternity in the empty void."

Picard's log informs us that the Enterprise is bringing supplies to the Beagle, but all contact was mysteriously lost. Riker has hailing frequencies opened and scanner sweeps performed, all to no avail. Their only hope is to go to the ship's last reported position and save anyone who might be left. Enterprise launches a probing vessel which arrives before she dies, and the crew quickly determines that the Beagle is dead. Riker puts the ship on full alert, and tells the captain that he's needed on the bridge. Once Picard arrives, he's told of the status of the Beagle, as well as the fact there is no damage to the ship, or any radiation residue trailers. Considering this, Picard tells him to prepare an Away Team, which Riker does, consisting of himself, Beverly, Geordi and Data.

Act One: The Away Team beams over in "form fitting spacesuits – the latest in 24th Century technology." As the team breaks up, Data, Geordi and Riker proceed to the bridge, where they find a body frozen to a chair (as a result of depressurizing). Riker asks Geordi to try and bring the ship's engines back on line, while Data has moved over to a console and realized that every aspect of the ship's computer memory was frozen solid, and therefore its information is irretrievable. Just as Riker starts to grow angry at this, he receives a communiqué from Beverly Crusher, who asks that he come down to sickbay.

In sickbay, life support has been restored, and Beverly removes her helmet, as does her assistant, Ames. Riker enters the area and is led to a frozen body, its chest exploded open. There is frozen blood everywhere. Beverly chalks it up to "explosive decompression" as a result of the ship's hatches being blown. Riker nears the body, but is told to stay away from it, as the risk of contamination does exist. It is Beverly's opinion that the hatches were blown in an attempt to destroy *something* which would have proven malignant to much more than just the crew of the Beagle.

Shortly thereafter, the Away Team reappears on the transporter platform aboard the Enterprise. They are decontaminated, and step off the platform. The bodies of corpses are placed on futuristic gurneys, with Riker telling Beverly that he wants a full report upon the completion of autopsies. She says it will be done right away, then notes that Ames doesn't look well, to which the man replies that he doesn't handle death very well. Beverly tells him to report to sickbay after completing his reports.

In the captain's ready room, Riker has detailed their discovery to Picard, who conjectures that the reason no one else was found on the Beagle is that they had never returned to the vessel. "Play this scenario," says Picard. "The Beagle sends a party down somewhere in the Aldebaran system and brings back some contaminant with them . . ." Riker picks up on his line of thought, adding that they must have returned to that world to find a cure, with the captain adding that they never made it back. Turning his attention to Geordi, he asks that they do everything they can to retrace the Beagle's travel route.

Back in sickbay, Beverly examines Ames, but chalks up his reaction to seeing death, and nothing more. Physically he seems alright, but she recommends that he come back to see her again in two days.

Bridge: Geordi tells Picard that thus far they've been able to narrow the trajectories of the Beagle down to twelve hundred, and that they'll try to limit it down further. Then the captain contacts sickbay, wanting a progress report from Beverly, who explains that the only cause of death was the explosive decompression. There is *no* sign of an inside influence which may have caused the ship's captain to blow the hatches. Riker is hooked on the idea of a contaminant, but admits that there really isn't any proof of such a disease. At that moment, Beverly mentions that everyone should go easy on Ames for the next few days, because he's having a hard time dealing with the dead bodies he saw on the Beagle. The channel is closed, with Picard pointing out that death can be hard on someone at any age, "especially if it's your own."

Act Two: Wes is trying to involve Ames in a game of chess-droids, but the other man isn't interested, exploding that they're in the middle of nowhere and the only thing keeping them from the harshness of space is the bulkhead of the ship that they occupy. "We don't belong here," he says. "It's not meant to be." Ames insists that the Enterprise crew is going to end up exactly like the Beagle's. A fight develops between them, but two crewmen come over and break them up. As the struggle grows more serious, Wes contacts security and then sickbay, requesting the presence of a medic.

In sickbay, Beverly is amazed at the change in Ames, noting that his white blood cell count is way above where it should be, but her real concern is over the way he's acting, which is why she contacted Troi. Some time later, Picard, Riker, Beverly and Troi meet in the bridge lounge, with the captain trying to determine just what is going on with Ames. Troi, unfortunately, has not been able to exert much of an effect on the man. When the captain snaps at her that he expects some answers, Beverly responds that she is doing the best that she can. Riker starts to cough, which immediately draws the doctor's attention due to the fact that the commander is one of those people who *never* gets sick. Beverly suspects that a disease is starting to spread. Troi disagrees, pointing out that they were all decontaminated when they beamed back aboard the Enterprise. "You can't decontaminate yourself for something you don't know exists," Beverly bluntly snaps back. Picard agrees, stating that the boarding party will have to be quarantined, but the doctor notes that it's too late for that. If there is a disease, it's already started to spread. She does, however, want the Away Team to report to sickbay for examinations. Picard orders Geordi to go to sickbay and after a moment's hesitation asks Wes to take over the task of limiting potential trajectories of the Beagle.

Sickbay: In the midst of examinations, Beverly asks Riker what he had for breakfast, but the commander can't come up with the answer. She then asks Geordi some trivia, which he answers immediately. He, then, can go back to his station, but Riker cannot return to the bridge. Riker and other members of the Away Team are told that they'll be prepped for surgery, based on what Beverly discovered during the last phase of the autopsies performed on the Beagle crewmembers. The doctor explains that she wants to perform a brain scan on Riker, and he muses that the cure is worse than the disease itself.

"Patients always think that way," is her response. "Especially ones with an exaggerated sense of self-importance."

"What's that supposed to mean?"

"It means this ship will survive without you for a while."

This passage of dialogue was re-printed because it rang so true to life, and would be a welcome exchange between the characters, striking a chord of realism akin to the old *Star Trek*. Simple, but effective.

There is a scream from Ames, but by the time Beverly has arrived the man is in the midst of a massive coronary, and all attempts to reverse it prove fruitless. Riker looks on in horror.

Act Three: Wes and Geordi inform Picard that they're "almost there" in terms of their research, thanks, in a large part, to Wes' contribution. Then summoned to sickbay, Picard learns that the captain of the Beagle was suffering from a brain infection, which resulted from a reduction of its immune abilities. Beverly terms it a cancer of the blood which eventually results in death. Using a medical device, she punches up the image of one of the dead men's insides, showing the green areas which indicate the places attacked by the virus. When the hatches of the Beagle were blown, not only were the bodies frozen, but so was the virus itself, which was unleashed when brought into the warmer atmosphere of the Enterprise. It is her belief that the virus can survive in the atmosphere for approximately two hours. Apparently the other ship contracted the disease while in the Aldebaran star system, which is probably the only place that they'll be able to find a cure. Picard asks her if she's alright, and the doctor replies that she's a carrier without any of the symptoms. So far Ames and Riker are the only other two infected.

Picard returns to the bridge, where the computer has finally been able to trace the trajectory of the Beagle. A course is laid in, and Enterprise is on her way. Going back to sickbay, the captain checks on Riker, who's growing weaker, and more paranoid, believing that they're all going to die. Beverly comes over with a hypo to calm him down, but the commander states that they're trying to kill him.

She's eventually successful, and Riker passes out. Then there is the sound of a struggle from another area of sickbay, where a crewman is screaming out that he won't let the "witch" use her black magic on him. Two members of security try to hold him at bay, but it isn't easy. One of the men explains that they caught this person with a thermite grenade, about to kill himself with it. Beverly tells them to strap him down in the ward. Once this is done, Picard has them return to their posts. Beverly fears things will grow worse before they get better, with the captain pessimistically wondering if they will *ever* get better.

Bridge: Enterprise is locking into orbit around Aldebaran IV, with Data starting to scan the planet. Tasha interjects that there are problems with various crewmembers on several decks. Beverly adds that there are twelve cases already in sickbay, and that they're beginning to lose control over the situation. Meanwhile in sickbay, Riker asks Davis, a med-tech, for some water, and tricks the man into opening his bonds. The commander immediately dispatches him and is on his feet, "a maniacal grin on his face."

Act Four: Ship scanners have detected a nuclear power source, which Data deduces to be a man-made structure. Beverly believes that that is the key they've been searching for. With Picard's permission, she has Data organize an Away Team, all of whom beam down mere moments later.

On the surface, they discover a research hut which was constructed by the crew of the Beagle, and within it they discover "three bodies mummified in the planet's dry air," which are deemed the other members of the Beagle crew. Back on the ship, Davis comes to and tells Tasha what happened, and she, in turn, alerts security to the fact that the commander is to be captured. Meanwhile, Riker dispatches someone else and steals the man's phaser before continuing on his journey through the ship.

Aldebaran IV: Data suggests that they burn the bodies to prevent the spread of disease, which Beverly concurs with. While he sees to it, she goes back within the hut and grabs various tapes and slides, which she crams into a viewer. Later, Picard contacts her and she explains that the Beagle crew had found a planet which might be able to reverse the effect of the virus, but they ran out of time before they could use it. She is going to try to finish what they started. Picard only asks that she hurry, as things are getting out of hand on board the Enterprise.

Enterprise: Riker enters auxiliary control, takes care of the guard on duty, and starts maneuvering various controls. On the bridge, Geordi receives an alert from the engineering deck. Tasha picks up on it, stating that auxiliary control has been "locked off," with the bio and warp systems being controlled from that area. Geordi informs them that there is no way to override it, and the news goes from bad to worse when Picard learns that Riker is the culprit. He tells Tasha to have a security team meet him at auxiliary control. Arriving there, the captain begs Riker to let him in, but the commander merely argues that they're all dying, and he's just helping everyone out by speeding up the process. Picard wants the doors to the area blown open, but one of the security guards states that doing so would prove damaging to the guidance control computers. He slams the man against a wall, demanding that he follow orders, and then pulls back as he realizes what he's doing. Regaining his senses, he tells the man to get a plasma engineer to cut through the door.

On the planet, Data watches the flames which have engulfed the three bodies they had discovered. He then steps within the research hut, only to find that Beverly is starting to fall under the influence of the disease, chastising him because he supposedly thinks he's above them all; because he's not dying like the rest of them. Data suggests that she not lose control, which she somehow manages to agree with. There is an alarm from a computer she's been working with, which indicates that her experiments are complete. She removes a vial of green fluid, and has Data inject it in her arm. A moment later she collapses to the floor.

Act Five: Beverly comes to with Data's assistance. A blood sample is taken, and they discover that the virus has been destroyed by the vaccine. She tries to contact the Enterprise, where, on the bridge, Geordi states that their orbit is starting to break up due to what Riker's been doing. Beverly gets through on a rapidly disintegrating communication channel. Picard orders the transporter room to beam up the Away Team. Geordi says that their orbit is decaying rapidly, and that hull temperature is now nine hundred degrees Kelvin. The word comes from the transporter room: the Away Team is aboard. Wes approaches Picard, stating that he has come up with a theory which will allow the Enterprise to sling-shot its way across the atmosphere of the planet, and then allow them to break out of orbit. The captain accepts what the boy has said, and his plan is put into motion. After an extremely dangerous moment or two, the starship ends up in space again, having narrowly avoided destruction. Then, Riker, who had been hauled out of auxiliary control, enters the bridge, trying to place himself under arrest for mutiny. Beverly follows and is joined by Data. In the turbolift, Beverly apologizes for what she had said to Data

on the surface, but he brushes it off by saying, "There are times we all do things we regret . . . it is, after all, what makes us . . . human."

On the bridge, Picard congratulates Wesley for his plan. Geordi states that the ship's warp engines are back to full capacity and, bearing that in mind, Picard orders the Enterprise to engage its engines at warp one.

* * *

Let's get a few criticisms out of the way first. The title of this script, "The Immunity Syndrome," is the same as one of the original show's episodes, which was a mistake on the author's part. In addition, the plotline of this story is *very* similar to *Star Trek*'s "The Naked Time," and *The Next Generation* remake, "The Naked Now," with a disease rapidly making its way through the Enterprise, altering the personalities of crewmembers and causing someone (in the former Kevin Riley, in the latter Wesley Crusher) to lock themselves off in a section of engineering and play havoc with the ship's engines. Yet despite all this, "The Immunity Syndrome" is an effective script, and probably would have been a vast improvement over the aired version of "The Naked Now." Writer JD Kurtz proves himself more than competent in handling the *Trek* universe, and most definitely deserves the opportunity to try his hand at another story. This tale is an involving one (despite the criticisms cited above), and the treatment of the characters is absolutely terrific. You really do believe just about everything they're saying, and we are made privy to some inner conflicts between them, which would have been welcome on the series itself. Kurtz definitely deserves kudos for this effort.

"THE CRYSTAL SKULL"
Written by Patrick Barry

Arriving at the desert planet Bolaxnu 7, located mid-way between Federation and Ferengi territory, the Enterprise is assigned the task of bringing supplies (yes ... supplies again. Amazing what a recurring theme this is) to an archaeological mission being led by Doctor Annette Boudreau. Elevating this mission above the mundane is the doctor's announcement that she has discovered a lost city which indicates that this world is "actually Izul, capital planet of the vast and powerful Faran Empire, which fell into an abrupt and mysterious collapse over eight thousand years ago."

An Away Team consisting of Riker, Data, Worf, Wesley and Beverly and a med-tech appear at the threshold of a pair of monoliths, which create a passage into the aforementioned city. Taking in their surroundings visually and via tricorder, Riker opens up a channel with the Enterprise and instructs the transporter room to beam down the supplies. Moments later, five supply modules materialize, just as Boudreau and two members from her team "appear" at the entrance. The woman's beauty, it's obvious, touches Riker. After introductions are over, she explains that a man named Roark was recently injured and she's concerned about him. When it's pointed out that Beverly is chief medical officer of the Enterprise, Boudreau leads her and Riker through the entrance and into the subterranean room, where the injured man lies. While the doctor is off taking care of him, Riker asks Boudreau about Izul, but is told that her proclamations may have been premature. She may have been wrong. Before the commander can discuss the issue further, she becomes distracted, and excuses herself.

Shortly thereafter, Riker is walking through an underground tunnel where he encounters Data and Worf, who have overseen the transfer of supplies. Data is particularly intrigued by this discovery, explaining that a distant colony of the Faran Empire which was stranded after it collapsed, was the Ferengi home world known as Bunol. This discovery could, theoretically, provide some tantalizing information pertaining to Ferengi culture. Reluctantly, Riker tells the android of Boudreau's claim that she may have been wrong in making the announcement in the first place. His curiosity piqued, Riker excuses himself and makes his way down to the doctor's chambers, where he sees her sitting down grasping a crystal skull, while apparently in a meditative and ecstatic state. As Riker enters the room, she starts shouting that he should leave and not come back, but he refuses. What, exactly, is the skull, is what he wants to know. While ordering him out, she moves to put the skull in hiding, but Riker reaches out, touches it and suddenly begins to smile as he pulls the skull from her hands.

Act One: All of Boudreau's attempts to take the skull back prove fruitless, so she gives in and asks Riker if he's going to share it with her. He says that he will in his own good time, and then starts to kiss her passionately. Needless to say, things aren't exactly right with the good commander.

On the Enterprise bridge, Geordi informs Picard that what appears to be Ferengi ship is approaching. Looking to Troi for some kind of an answer, the Betazoid only tells him that she can feel obsession, but doesn't know where it's coming from or what it pertains to. Considering all of this, Picard contacts Riker, informs him of the Ferengi vessel and states that the Away Team should be ready to beam up at a moment's notice.

Back on the surface, Boudreau is concerned that the Ferengi are out for revenge against them because of the historical value of this place. Riker tells her that everything is going to be fine, as he places the skull in a leather bag and embraces her. Later, the two of them proceed to the subterranean chamber we had seen earlier, where they join the rest of the Away and archaeological teams. Once there, Data begins to discuss the connection between the Ferengi and the Faran Empire, as well as the philosophy of the Faran's emperor, Doshin, who was, according to the treatment, "actually a succession of rulers, all of whom took the same name and had one thing in common: the possession of a crystal skull said to have mysterious powers." All of these emperors of Izul did a great deal of writing, which aided, in some part, to the formation of the Ferengi society. An additional fact supplied by the android is that the Ferengi took to Izul in the same way that Earth people took to Camelot, with the skull, then, being an equivalent to the Holy Grail. Turning his attention to Boudreau, he asks if she is at all familiar with the legend of the crystal skull, to which she responds in the affirmative, although it is her understanding that it was destroyed thousands of years ago.

Picard contacts Riker, telling him that due to the denseness of the tunnels, the transporter is unable to lock on to the archaeologists, and the signal from the Away Team is extremely low. The Ferengi are still approaching, so they have to beam those people with communicators up first, and the rest must proceed to the surface where sensors will be able to lock on to them. The channel closed, Riker places his communicator on the injured man, and then asks Worf to place his on Boudreau, which the Klingon does. Although Wes wants to give his insignia to an archaeologist, his mother points out that the boy has never had any training in combat. Riker agrees. Ultimately, Wes, Beverly, a med-tech, Boudreau and the wounded man are beamed up, with Riker telling everyone else that they're going to have to move up to the surface.

Enterprise: the starship has received a communiqué from the Ferengi vessel, captained by Zaeb, who claims that Picard is heading a spy mission. Actually amused by this claim, Picard asks him how he came to this rather remarkable conclusion, and Zaeb responds that they had picked up a transmission from a Federation "agent" named Boudreau, who bragged over her discovery of the crystal skull. This is followed by the proclamation that the planet now belongs to the Ferengi, and all members of the Federation had best vacate it. Picard counters that since his people were the first to chart this system, theoretically it should belong to the Federation. This is interrupted by Geordi, who announces the beam-down of a Ferengi landing party. Turning his attention back to Zaeb (and sounding very much like our old friend James T. Kirk), the captain warns that if harm should come to *anyone*, the price extracted will be a high one.

Making their way through the tunnels, Riker and company run into the Ferengi landing party and the "blue-skinned oriental looking Kakiri Warriors," who level their weapons at our people. Riker merely smiles in response.

Act Two: Luug (are they kidding?), the commander of the Ferengi team, tells Riker that he and his people are now prisoners of the Alliance, and instructs them to turn over their weapons. Riker's response is to laugh, as he confidently replies that he knows that the Ferengi have come for the crystal skull, an item which he has already obtained and hidden. Any moves on the part of the Ferengi or the accompanying warriors will cause Riker to trigger a thermonuclear device he has hidden in the underground realm. The commander

adds that Picard must take part in the final negotiations which will occur within the hour. Luug, not wanting to chance losing out on the skull, agrees to Riker's terms. Turning his attention to Data, Riker tells him to move everyone else outside so that they can be beamed up. The android is also instructed to have Captain Picard and Doctor Boudreau beamed down in an hour.

Once everyone but Worf has gone, Riker turns to the Klingon and instructs him to check on the "device," which Worf, going along with Riker's plan, turns to do. Once he is alone, the commander turns back to Luug and tells him that he and Picard would be interested in some "goodwill unofficial trading" that would make the crystal skull seem like a mere trinket. He goes on to impress the alien by speaking of Ferengi philosophy, and as the conversation develops there seems to be a chord struck between these two.

On the bridge, Data has detailed Riker's instructions to Picard, who is confused by all of this. The only way to get the answers he needs is to beam down to the planet's surface.

Back on the planet, Worf compliments Riker concerning the way he handled the Ferengi, although he is a bit bothered by the fact that the commander had essentially gone against honor codes taken at the Academy by lying to the Ferengi about possession of the skull and the thermonuclear device. While this seems a serious point with the Klingon, Riker brushes it off, chalking it up to a plan that he has, which will be explained to Picard as soon as the captain beams down. Changing the subject, he tells Worf to check some of the back tunnels to see if they might possibly lead to the surface, so that they have an escape route should something go wrong with the scheduled meeting.

Shortly thereafter, Picard, Troi, Tasha, security agents and Boudreau appear in the underground chamber,

and are surprised to find neither Riker nor Worf anywhere. The captain calls out, not realizing that Riker is currently in Boudreau's quarters, the skull in his hands and his expression betraying a meditative state. But Picard's voice cuts into his concentration, and he places the skull back in the leather shoulder bag, which he hides elsewhere. From there he steps into the central hall where everyone is waiting for him. Boudreau runs up to him and wants to know if what she's heard regarding the Ferengi and the skull is true, but Riker merely smiles at her reassuringly. When Picard wants some answers, the commander side-steps, stating that the two of them and Data will be the only ones involved in the negotiations. No security and no Betazoids. Boudreau will also join them, as she has a working knowledge of the planet and its history.

Back in sickbay, Roark comes to for a moment, looking at Beverly and saying something about the crystal skull and that a woman must be stopped. Unfortunately the doctor cannot make any sense out of this statement. We shift back underground, where the group is about to be left alone. Before the others go, Riker approaches Deanna Troi and tells her that there is something he wishes to speak to her of; feelings he wants to express that he has never been able to express before. Then Picard says it's time for them to proceed. The remaining members of the group start making their way through the tunnel, when Riker suddenly knocks out Data (exactly how is never explained), and Boudreau takes care of the captain. The communicators are taken from their uniforms, as well as their phasers. Boudreau is delighted, pointing out that they will have the skull to share between the two of them. Riker has other plans, as he knocks her out as well. Leaving the area, he utilizes his phaser to create a cave-in that effectively seals everyone within.

Riker moves back into the doctor's quarters where he retrieves the bag containing the skull and moves out of the area. Proceeding into the outer chamber, he encounters Worf, who has joined up with the security team, and explains that the Kakiri betrayed them and murdered Picard, Data and Boudreau. Saying that they have no alternative, Riker has them beamed back up to the Enterprise.

Act Three: Back on the bridge, Worf is absolutely furious at what has happened with the Ferengi. Riker does his best to placate him, while ordering Geordi to raise the Ferengi captain. Zaeb's image appears, and Riker angrily chastises him for the attack on personnel from the Federation. Naturally the alien has no idea of what the human (or hu-man, as they like to say) is talking about. Riker's curt response is that the Ferengi ship had better surrender within ten minutes, or it will be destroyed. The channel is closed. The ship is brought to red alert status, and certain members of the bridge crew take note of the fact that he seems to be *anticipating* the imminent battle.

Underground: Data awakens, and quickly revives the captain and doctor, as all three try to figure out exactly what happened. Boudreau, furious that Riker has betrayed her, spills the proverbial beans, and tells them everything she knows about the skull and its effect. We quote, "The skull overwhelms you with pleasure, like a drug, until it controls you . . . then you become one with the will of Doshin, and you are its tool."

Naturally the first course of action is to set themselves free, and to this end Data starts removing rubble, but even for him it will take hours. Boudreau remembers a laser shovel nearby, and digs it out. They utilize it to speed their progress.

Enterprise: Troi tells Riker that she sensed anger and confusion in Zaeb. Still confident, the commander believes that the Ferengi chose the wrong man to "mess" with. He moves over to hug her, but she is re-sistant, pointing out that her main concern at the moment is the problem at hand, and the fact that Captain Picard is dead (although shouldn't she be able to tell that Will is lying to her? She should have some sort of sense of dishonesty about the commander). Troi leaves the room. Meanwhile, in sickbay, Roark has come to again, and is telling Beverly of the skull and the effect it's had on Boudreau, and that she is the one who actually pushed him into the pit where he was injured. Beverly tells him of what's happened, and notes, almost to herself, how Riker seems to have changed. It is Roark's opinion that the commander must be under the influence of the skull as well. Calling a private meeting between herself, Troi and Wes, Beverly explains what she's discovered and what she believes to be wrong with Number One. Bearing all the evidence in mind, perhaps the captain is still alive on the planet somewhere, she suggests. Troi "tunes in" to the planet, and definitely senses that there is life there.

Beverly asks her son whether or not it would be possible to contact the planet without alerting the bridge to the fact, and he believes that he'll be able to bypass the main communication controls, although there's no assurance that such a move wouldn't be detected. He sets off on his own, while Troi says she'll return to the bridge and do whatever she can to keep Riker under control. On the bridge, Riker, who suddenly seems to be growing fatigued, tells the Ferengi captain to get his people off the planet's surface immediately, because he will be demonstrating the Enterprise's power by destroying the underground city. The order is given to Worf: aim photon torpedoes at the heart of Izul.

Act Four: Riker, who has ap-parently moved himself into Picard's quarters, sits with the skull in his hands. Worf, who like everyone else doesn't seem to be questioning Rik-er's decision to destroy the underground city, pipes in on the communication channel, reminding the commander that he's awaiting the order to fire. Riker comes out of meditation and says he'll be right there. By the time he returns to the bridge, Number One seems com-pletely rejuvenated, and "ready to destroy." Troi approaches him, stat-ing that this course of action may not be the right one. His only response is to smile as he turns to Worf to give the order. Troi touches his hand, say-ing that they should have some time together before things start to "heat up." Agreeing, he leaves the bridge with her. Meanwhile, Wes has made his way into a Jeffries Tube, and man-ages to send a signal down to the planet. Boudreau is the one who manages to pick it up on the archae-ological team's communications system. Picard gets on the channel, desperately seeking information as to what's going on. The boy quickly ex-plains, and Picard says that he and the others will get to the surface so they can be beamed aboard.

Riker and Troi, in the meantime, have gone to the captain's room, when Geordi contacts the com-mander, explaining that there has been unauthorized transmission from the ship. Furious, he makes his way back to the bridge, ranting of spies running rampantly aboard the Enter-prise and wanting to find the person guilty of unauthorized communica-tion to be brought to him immediately. Riker orders the destruc-tion of the city, but is interrupted by Troi's objections and contact from the Ferengi vessel, with Zaeb demanding that the Enterprise either depart this area of space of make the first move against them. The com-mander is delighted by the challenge.

Beverly and Wes get into the transporter room, and beam up their people just as the Kakiri Warriors are surrounding them. Riker, who is still on the bridge, is shocked when he hears Picard's voice speaking to him over the comm channel. His immediate response is that the Ferengi have cloned Picard and the others, and somehow devised a way to get them on the Enterprise without being detected. There's no choice: they must be destroyed!

Act Five: Angry, Riker goes to the captain's quarters and grabs the crystal skull, which he brings with him back to the bridge. He tells Worf that the crew can't be trusted, and he wants the Klingon to join him. They move into the turbo lift, which brings them to the battle bridge. Troi tells the captain, via intercom, that Riker has gone to the battle bridge, and that the situation between the Enterprise and the Ferengi vessel is heating up. Then, Geordi makes the discovery that Riker and Worf have cut off the turbo lift, essentially stranding themselves in the battle bridge, and keeping everyone else out. Picard's instinct is that Riker is going to separate the saucer section from the rest of the ship (see the "Encounter at Farpoint" premiere episode of *The Next Generation* or the feature film *Star Trek: Generations* for full details on how this is done). The captain wants to be beamed onto the battle bridge, but the operator tells him that Riker has erected a force field which will repel all attempts.

Battle bridge: Riker wants Worf to separate from the saucer section, open fire on the city and prepare to engage the Ferengi vessel. Even the Klingon has some problems with this. Riker merely smiles, pointing out that this is a day that will seal their destinies, and will no doubt result in their each receiving their own commands. Before Worf can respond, Picard's image appears on the main viewer,

the captain trying desperately to talk Riker out of this dangerous action. The commander tells Worf to cut off the channel, but the Klingon doesn't do it as Picard tells Will to think for himself; to try to overcome the influence of the skull that is controlling him. Riker tries to laugh this claim of control off, but he starts glancing at the bag containing the skull "thirstily." Moving towards the bag, he tells Worf to open fire, but the Klingon merely asks what's in the bag. Again Riker is furious, trying to get past Worf so that he himself can launch the photon torpedoes, but Worf pulls him away. Naturally the Klingon is turning out victorious, but Riker grabs the skull and his strength is instantly renewed. The skull is knocked out of his hand. Riker grabs a phaser and fires, but Worf is too quick, and the beam finds its mark on the skull. No sooner has this happened, than Riker collapses to the ground. According to the treatment, "the skull is now revealed to have a blackened, burned out core with a cracked crystal coating."

Later, on the bridge, Picard is back in command, with Worf bringing him what's left of the skull for his inspection. Data's scanners indicate that there is no longer any power in it. Beverly pipes in, stating that Riker is going to be okay, and he'll be in control of his own mind.

As word reaches the captain that the Ferengi force has beamed back up, he has Tasha assemble her own people and beam down, then contacting Zaeb and firmly explaining that they are on an official Federation mission, and if any further Ferengi forces beam down it will be seen as an act of aggression. Zaeb wants an explanation for Riker, but the captain

rather smugly says there's no reason to explain anything. He also mentions that they do not have the crystal skull. Zaeb considers this for a moment, flares with anger, and then Enterprise sensors detect the Ferengi vessel breaking orbit and setting off for deep space.

In sickbay, Riker comes to and finds Picard, Troi, Worf and Beverly standing around him. He tries to apologize for everything that happened, but Picard says that his actions were successful in getting the Ferengi off the planet, and that in itself has to be worth something. They'll discuss everything else at a later time.

* * *

While there are some serious problems with this story, "The Crystal Skull" would have made an interesting and highly effective episode of *Star Trek: The Next Generation*, had it been developed further. While there are certain plot problems and a number of story contrivances (which, again, would have been corrected had the writer – who, incidentally, wrote "Angel One" for the first season – moved to teleplay with it), there is also an inherent feel of suspense in regards to Riker. It would have been interesting to see a subtle change in the commander that gradually became more pronounced as time went on, until the point where he was being fully possessed by the crystal skull. One can only assume that actor Jonathan Frakes would have welcomed the opportunity to stretch his acting abilities with this unique approach to the character of Will Riker.

"BLOOD AND FIRE"
Written by David Gerrold

The Enterprise approaches the U.S.S. Copernicus, a scientific research vessel which had sent out a distress signal and is now adrift with no further communication coming from its captain or crew. An Away Team consisting of Riker, Tasha, Geordi, Freeman and Eakins (which, incidentally, is the name author David Gerrold gave to the main character in the "Man out of Time" episode of the *Logan's Run* television series). A man named Hodel is with Worf at the transporter console (bear in mind that this script was written when things were still being set up, so it's possible that Worf would have been the transporter chief), before he joins the others at the platform, patting Eakins affectionately on the shoulder.

Picard suggests that Beverly, if she wants to, can monitor the medical team's progress from the bridge, while Worf points out that scanners are picking up a repulsor field located at the center of the other ship's cargo bay. Picard quickly deduces that the crew of the Copernicus is obviously trying to isolate something.

Act One: The Away Team materializes in a darkened corridor of the other starship (described as a redress of the movie Enterprise sets). In mid-air there is the flickering of pink and gold, but the image is described as being almost subliminal. Geordi points out that the ship monitor systems must be down, as they hear absolutely nothing. Riker catches a glimpse of the flicker again, and Geordi describes them as being "some kind of wavicle." The flickers move around Geordi and then vanish, filling him with a tickling sensation. Freeman, who has been utilizing his tricorder, cannot explain what they've just seen. Meanwhile, on the Enterprise bridge, Picard and Data, who have been watching everything via the viewscreen, get to work on the

flickers. Back on the Copernicus, the Away Team finds their passage in the corridor blocked off by doors which have been permanently sealed. Considering this, Riker tells them that they'll be using manual access to the bridge. Data contacts, explaining that he is picking up extremely weak readings of life throughout the ship, but he is unable to locate all of them.

They move onto the bridge, and Geordi screams out as he takes in the sight of a mummified crewman who they deduce was responsible for sending out the distress signal. Freeman approaches, takes tricorder readings and makes the shocked discovery that the body contains absolutely no blood. Hodel jokingly refers to the body as a victim of a space vampire. Riker has Geordi download the Copernicus' log to their tricorders as well as the Enterprise, while everyone else makes their way around the bridge, quickly discovering that all of the consoles have been destroyed by phaser fire. At that moment, Data announces that the previously detected life form is headed right for the bridge. Seconds later, the turbo lift doors open, admitting Ahrens, who is described as looking very haggard and sick. While everyone instinctively takes a step back, Freeman moves towards the man, tricorder outstretched. Ahrens starts ranting that they're too late, and that everyone is already dead.

Removing a hypo-spray from his med-kit, Freeman injects the man with a tranquilizer, but at that moment Ahrens screams out in pain, begging them to kill him quickly. The man collapses to the deck, a red stain spreading across his chest. Tasha starts her report to Enterprise, when Data interrupts, stating that the life forms are *still* moving towards them. Then, Ahrens manages to grab Geordi's phaser and unleashes a lethal blast at himself, disintegrating his body and leaving, in the aftermath, a cloud of pink and gold wavicles similar to the ones we had seen earlier,

which spread out quickly, move into the Away Team and then vanish. Riker, speaking to Picard, states his opinion that the whole ship – including them – is probably infected with whatever killed the Copernicus crew. From the Enterprise bridge, Beverly suggests that they utilize the transporter's bio-filters, but the commander points out that the device will not filter out wavicles. There simply is no way for them to beam back. The captain turns to Troi, who says that the survivors of the Copernicus may have isolated themselves within the repulsor field detected in the cargo-bay, and perhaps some answers will be found there. Riker informs Picard that it's a possibility they're going to investigate.

A moment later, Data and Beverly ask to speak to the captain alone, and as the trio move away from the main viewscreen, Data explains that the problem which seems to have affected the Copernicus is plasmasites, also known as blood-worms. They've learned that the only other case of plasmasites that they're aware of took place on a world within the Regulan system, which has been quarantined for the past century and a half. Picard doesn't want the situation discussed any further, and when Data points out that Starfleet regulations prohibit even attempted rescues of potential victims, Picard feels there must be a solution that they can reach. Beverly, hating to be the one to do so, drops the other shoe: there is *no* cure known for the disease, because it has never left any survivors.

Act Two: Hodel and Eakins work on a computer console, doing their best to reactivate it. Hodel locates the proper connection and contacts the Enterprise to begin downloading information. The man is then shocked to find a red worm slithering across a cable. The worm is removed and placed in a sample case, as Hodel reaches back into the panel and yelps in pain as something hurts him.

Extracting his hand, he and Eakins are horrified to find several more of the bloodworms. Eakins contacts Riker, and as he does so a wave of the worms start slithering down the panels and out into the open. Hodel, meanwhile, is finding it impossible to get rid of the worms on his hand as others start attaching themselves to different parts of his body. Eakins fires his phaser into a group of the worms on the floor, and they transform into wavicles. He backs away in horror as Hodel is nearly covered in worms, and ultimately decides to use his phaser to put the man out of his misery. A large cloud of wavicles results from the man's disintegration.

Needless to say, this is one hell of an intense scene, and really quite a horrifying one. The only episode to even come close in terms of generating pure terror that actually made it to the air was "Conspiracy," which dealt with a worm threat of a different kind.

At that moment, Riker and Tasha come up behind Eakins and without asking any questions, decide that the best course of action would be to run to safety. Corridor doors are closed, with the hope being that the worms will not be able to make their way through them. Freeman, meanwhile, has joined them. Picard contacts them, explains that the enemy is definitely Regulan blood worms, and this announcement extracts reactions which convey that the Away Team knows for sure what *that* means. Things go from bad to worse, when Riker notices several of the worms managing to squeeze their way over the top of the closed doors. Picard tells them Enterprise scanners have detected that entire section of the Copernicus are infested with the worms, so the Away Team will be transported to the middle of the repulsor field within the cargo bay. When rematerialization is complete, they find themselves with fifteen haggard survivors. Two crewmembers, Yarell and Blodgett, approach them while Freeman goes to work on the

others, doing his best to ease their pain. Introductions are handled quickly, with Riker immediately asking Yarell if he allowed the Copernicus to violate the Regulan quarantine. The man responds that this mission was an authorized one designed to discern if it would be possible to neutralize the threat of plasmasite infestation.

Blodgett interjects the initial spores are drawn to oxygen-binding enzymes exactly like those which are found in human blood, and once there they metamorphosize into the bloodworms. Geordi approaches, pointing out that the repulsor field – their only means of safety – is completely surrounded by the bloodworm threat, and that the energy for the field will only remain strong enough to repel them for a short time longer.

Back on the Enterprise bridge, Beverly theorizes a way in which a person could be saved by having *all* of the blood removed from their body, thus killing the bloodworms, and then replacing it with fresh blood. Needless to say, this would be an extremely dangerous gamble, and anyone partaking would have no more than ten minutes for the transfusion to be complete or that person would die. Their conversation is interrupted by Yarell, who refers to a particular Starfleet regulation which states that "critically important" personnel must be rescued from a hostile situation before anyone else. Riker argues that the sick people near them are the ones who need to be helped first, but Picard, unfortunately, is forced to side with Yarell. Picard turns to where Beverly was a moment ago, but now she's gone. Data states that she's gone to the transporter room.

Angry, Picard goes to the transporter room, where he tries to dissuade Beverly from beaming over to the Copernicus, siting the dangerous situation and using the fact that she's an only parent as an excuse. She

feels that such a remark is beneath him, while adding that she and Wesley have discussed the danger of their mission many times in the past. But if she does not beam over to that other ship to help those people, then her oath as a physician is meaningless. She steps on the platform, and is beamed over by Worf. Once she's gone, the captain looks to the Klingon as though asking for his opinion.

"You're asking me as a Klingon?" he replies. "Beat her. As a professional . . . she was right."

Picard agrees, and we've got a great joke from Worf.

Act Three: The crewmember at the Con position, tells Picard that the families on board don't want the captain to proceed with the rescue mission, for fear that the disease will spread throughout the Enterprise. Sounding very much like good old Captain Kirk, Picard replies that the Enterprise does not operate on a democratic basis. "We're not abandoning our shipmates," he says simply. "And we're not throwing away half the human race because the other half is scared."

Worf contacts Beverly on the Copernicus, telling her that the auxiliary sickbay is now ready. Yarell and Blodgett are being prepared to beam over to the Enterprise, with the doctor informing them that their bodies will be filled with artificial blood once they're over there. Before they depart, she asks where the bloodworms come from, and is told that they were created as a doomsday weapon to be used in a Regulan war. At that moment, the two men disappear in the transporter beam. Geordi, who seems to be the bearer of just wonderful news throughout the story, informs everyone that in about forty minutes the repulsor field will fail.

Enterprise: Wesley walks on to the bridge, where Picard tells him that he thought the boy might like to monitor his mother's progress with the rest of them. Wes wants to know if

Picard is trying to prepare him for something terrible, as the captain isn't usually so friendly. Then he asks for a rationale as to why Starfleet sends whole families into space when there are so many dangers which abound.

"Because," says Picard, "our ancestors took their children with them when they crossed the oceans in ships and the continents in covered wagons. Because – you *are* our children and we cannot leave you behind."

This passage of dialogue, as simple as it may be, really is quite wonderful, and taps into what the basic premise of *Star Trek* was all about in the first place. When Gene Roddenberry created the show, the idea was to do "Wagon Train to the Stars," and that fact has never been expressed as clearly as it is here.

Intercutting between Data on the Enterprise and Beverly on the smaller ship, they discuss the fact that they cannot destroy the bloodworms because they merely become wavicles which spread the infestation. As she states, "Suppose the plasmasites were deliberately mutated to keep them from metabolizing the enzymes they need. Is it possible to neutralize that infection?" Freeman then approaches, says they've got a problem and Beverly, in turn, contacts Picard, explaining that there will not be enough artificial blood for them to provide complete transfusions. They will have to collect blood from donors aboard the Enterprise. The captain makes the announcement to the crew of his vessel, stating that the donation of blood will not hurt, and sure "as hell" will help.

Act Four: As Data tells Picard that the Copernicus logs are incomplete, Yarell and Blodgett enter the bridge and are motioned towards the ready room. Once there, Picard demands to have some answers. Finally, Yarell admits that he was the one who authorized the Copernicus mission, emphasizing that there is an undeclared state of war existing between the Federation and the Ferengi Alliance, and he is extremely fearful of what would happen should that alien race decide to unleash the threat of the bloodworms into Federation territory. Their mission was to find a way to contain plasmasite infestation. Blodgett interjects that they had made a tremendous amount of progress in their studies, but Data is quick to add that there is no such evidence in the logs. Yarell takes the blame for that as well, explaining that they could not take the chance of their studies falling into Ferengi hands.

Picard, who has taken all of this in, points out that the Enterprise is not a military vessel – despite the fact that one of the ship's assignments is to defend allies – and that he is concerned about the plasmasite study, because if a weapon exists, invariably so does the temptation to use it. Yarell's response is that they cannot afford to be second best to anyone. Picard has security escort the two men to their quarters, ordering them to stay there.

Once the captain and Data have moved back to the bridge, the android explains that Geordi and Tasha have been beamed aboard since their transfusion has been completed, and that they will soon be followed by Riker and Freeman. Eakins will be last. On the Copernicus, Freeman and Eakins are arguing over who should beam back over to the Enterprise first. Freeman decides to end the argument by injecting Eakins and Riker with the enzyme suppressant. Before he slips into unconsciousness, Eakins hands Freeman his phaser, "just in case." Riker and Eakins disappear in the transporter beam.

No sooner are the two men gone, than the sound of the repulsor field weakens considerably, and then shuts down completely. Picard, who has been informed of this, has the transporter room on standby. Freeman contacts the bridge, telling them that he can hear the sound of the bloodworms approaching. Con points out that they've locked on to the man, but the medical tricorder reveals that he is still infected by the plasmasites. Realizing what's going on, Eakins calls out to his friend, but Freeman merely apologizes and starts to scream before there is the sound of a single phaser burst, signifying the end of the man's life. The communication channel is filled with static, which Picard disgustedly orders turned off.

Act Five: While Riker and Eakins are recovering in the auxiliary sickbay, Beverly goes to the bridge, pointing out that their problems aren't over yet. If the Copernicus is destroyed, there is a chance that they would be unleashing an incredible number of wavicles into deep space which would eventually locate a world with blood-filled beings, and the horror would start all over again. Data points out that the possibility is unlikely, but it does indeed exist. Beverly believes that the plasmasites are desperately trying to become something else, and their inability to metamorphosize is the thing that makes them so vicious. It is her opinion that she and Blodgett have come up with a way to alter that which makes the plasmasites hungry, which could then, theoretically, allow them to move to the next step of their evolution. The main problem is that the only way to test this cure is to use a human volunteer.

Naturally another problem arises as Data calculates the Copernicus' heading. Furious, Picard summons Yarell to the bridge. Once there, the bombshell is dropped: the Copernicus is headed for the heart of Ferengi space. The man finally admits that he has studied the Ferengi menace for fifteen years, and this would be the perfect way to obliterate that threat; by infiltrating their territory with the bloodworms. Yarell adds that the Enterprise is supposed to defend Federation space, but Picard believes that this is nothing more than blind hatred using defense as a cover. As the captain calls for security, Yarell removes a repulsor jar containing plasmasites, which he will unleash unless they are brought into Ferengi space. Seeing no alternative, Picard has Worf (who is now back on the bridge – wish they'd stop bouncing this poor Klingon around) lay in a course, but Worf responds that "number two engine is still down for dilithium recalibration. We can't run it with a hot warp." Snapping at the Klingon, Picard turns to Yarell and explains that there will be a short delay, but the man confidently points out that if nothing else he is extremely patient.

Eakins is suddenly before them, phaser leveled at Yarell, accusing the man of murdering all of the people on board the Copernicus, including Freeman. Picard steps in the way of the weapon, ordering Eakins to lower it, but the man refuses. Riker approaches, telling him to let Starfleet take care of Yarell in the way it should be done. A few tense moments pass, and, while weeping, Eakins hands his phaser to the commander. Then Yarell is screaming out, and as everyone turns to look, they see that Blodgett has taken the vial and is actually swallowing the plasmasites. He asks to be beamed over the Copernicus. Picard wants the man taken to sickbay, but he refuses, stating that he made a mistake by believing in Yarell, and now this is his opportunity to make up for that mistake. This will give them an opportunity to test the cure that Beverly has come up with.

Ultimately he is beamed over to the other ship, and once there all of the wavicles swarm over his body and into it. Ultimately he is transformed into a "beautiful glowing cloud of color and light and flickering sparkles. It is an Epiphany for him – a redemption." Blodgett then disappears into the light, and the result is a virtual light show with accompanying music as the wavicles actually begin singing in their own way.

On the bridge, Wesley, who is shocked at what he's seeing, refers to the sight before him as a legendary sparkle-dancer. The light explodes outward, rejoins in space and sets off as a "colony of dancing butterflies of light and energy." The Enterprise sets off for its next mission.

* * *

One aspect of the original *Star Trek* that has allowed it to withstand the passage of time, was its uncanny ability to combine thought-provoking and *meaningful* storylines with an entertainment format. "Blood and Fire" was David Gerrold's attempt to do so, tackling head-on the AIDS crisis and our reaction as a society to it.

Gerrold, known throughout fandom as the author of "Trouble With Tribbles," at one time spoke at a *Star Trek* convention, discussing his involvement with the new show, as well as the genesis of "Blood and Fire."

"The title of this talk is 'Blood and Fire – The Script You Won't See on *Star Trek*,'" Gerrold told the audience. "I have to do this very delicately. It was said of me last week that I never wrote anything useful for *Star Trek: The Next Generation*, because I'm too old to write for *Star Trek*, which I thought was a rather remarkable thing to say, particularly coming from the man who said it. I thought, 'You could insult me as a person all you want, and I'll probably agree with you, because I know what it's like to live with me. But when you talk about my passion for writing or the quality of my writing, then you're talking about something serious.' I thought what I would do is talk to you about how this script got written.

"*Star Trek: The Next Generation* was announced on October 10th, and I was hired on October 20th, and I was immediately involved with a lot of development work," he continued. "I wrote the first draft of the bible for Gene and I also did the final draft, and that was probably one of the most exciting and happiest experiences I had working on the show. Gene and I had long meetings about the characters, who would do what and how it would work out. At that time, Gene was a writer's dream of a producer, because he was available for input, listening to things people said and incorporated lots of good suggestions. As we started going, Gene suggested that I start thinking of story ideas, which I did.

"I don't know how other writers work, but let me tell you how it happens with me. There are things I want to write about and things I want to address, and sometimes they all fall into the same story at the same time. One story I started thinking about dealt with a planet of very religious, puritanical people and we have an observer living on that planet pretending to be one of them and they're about to burn him at the stake. In order to rescue him, we accidentally beam up not only him, but several people who are about to light the fire. Of course they end up in the transporter room, and all of these very religious people think that they've been transported to heaven. The problem for the Enterprise was going to be, 'How do we tell these people the truth without violating the Prime Directive and shattering their religion and culture, and how do we return them without also interfering with their culture?' The idea being that if we send them back, they can say they've been to heaven and have seen God. So we were working on that idea, and Dorothy Fontana suggested that the story be postponed, and that was because some of the other stuff we had in the works was a little soft, and she thought I should work on the action story I had also been playing with.

"What I wanted to do was deal with Regulan bloodworms, because we had mentioned them in 'Trouble With Tribbles.' People were always asking about them, but who knows what a Regulan bloodworm is? At that particular time there was a lot in the news about the AIDS panic and people not donating blood. Blood donorship was a major issue for me and always has been, and to hear that donorship was down because of fear of AIDS exposure, I wanted to do a story where at some point maybe everybody on the Enterprise must roll up their sleeves to donate blood to save the lives of some of their crewmembers. I thought, 'There's an interesting notion for a story.' So that was floating around in my head. Also, we had had a discussion of whether or not we could use Mike Minor as our art director. Unfortunately, Mike was very sick with AIDS at the time and has since passed away, which is a great loss to us. He worked on the *Star Trek* features, and had been involved in many different ways. I thought, 'Here's an issue we really ought to address.' I thought I would do a story that asked the question, 'What do you do with an infected population?' All of this is floating around in my mind. But let me give you the rest of the source material.

"In November of '86, we all — Gene and I, George Takei, Robin Curtis and some others — were at a convention in Boston called Platinum Anniversary. It was a 20th Anniversary celebration, and they had invited us all before they knew there was going to be a *Star Trek: The Next Generation*, so we all went out there and they were thrilled, because we were able to talk about what we planned to do on the new show, and they were very excited.

"There is apparently a gay science fiction club in Boston and they said, 'Gene, we've always had on *Star Trek* in the past, minorities clearly represented, isn't it time we had a gay crewmember on the Enterprise?' He said, 'You're probably right, sooner or later we'll have to address the issue and I'll have to give serious thought to it.' I thought, 'Okay, fine,' because I was sitting in the back

taking notes. Whatever Gene said was going to be policy. We came back to Los Angeles and I'm still making notes for the bible and other things, and we're at a meeting with Eddie Milkis, Bob Justman, John D.F. Black, Gene and myself, and Gene said, 'We should probably have a gay character on *Star Trek*. We seriously have to be willing to address the issue.' So I said, 'Okay, now I know that Gene seriously meant what he said in Boston, and I know that that's story material we could do.'

"At that time, I felt very positive, because by saying we could do that kind of story, Gene was also indicating a willingness to do a whole range of story material. As a writer I was excited, not just by that particular idea, but by the whole range of story ideas that were available. All of this is floating around in my head. I wanted to do a story that somehow acknowledged the AIDS fear, something with blood donorship, and I started blocking out a story called 'Blood and Fire' about Regulan bloodworms, and where it started was with the idea that we find a ship that has been infected, and if you have a starship that is infected, what do you do without bringing the infection to your own ship? I thought we should make it a really horrendous thing that there's a standing Starfleet order that when you run into a ship that's infected with bloodworms, the order is to destroy that ship immediately, because it is the merciful thing to do and the last three ships that tried to save an infected population were also infected and died horribly.

"In the first few stories written, we saw that they were a little soft and there wasn't much action, and to balance that I wanted to do a show that had a lot of hard action and adventure in it. So the idea is that they could find another ship infected with bloodworms and they have a major problem, and to make it even more serious — first the Away Team beams over and then they find out the ship is

infected with bloodworms. *Now* we have a problem. That's where I started, then I worked out the lifecycle of the bloodworms, that they grow in your blood until they reach a certain point and then, like malaria, they explode and start looking for new flesh. It was a very graphic kind of suggestion. I had a lot of fun with it, Dorothy liked it and Herb Wright loved it, saying that it was the kind of story we needed to do.

"I knew there were going to be major questions that you the audience would be asking about the new show, so I wanted to address a couple of those concerns [*reads scenes from the script which detail character moments, many of which were discussed in the preceding synopsis*]. I was having some fun with the script based on some of the things that you had been asking at the conventions.

"[There is only one scene that] deals with the relationship between Freeman and Eakins, and if you don't know better, they're just good friends. I wrote that in a way to acknowledge the contribution that gay people have made to the show and acknowledge that they were all taking a large part of the burden for the AIDS epidemic, because this story was an AIDS allegory. Then we deal with blood donation.

"I'm not going to tell you how it ends, because I think the ending is real nice. It's a very grim story and had it been shot the way it was written — or shot at all — there's a very satisfying ending that is truly a *Star Trek* ending, and part of it is that we don't truly understand who or what the bloodworms are, and there are things we don't understand that we have to learn. I won't spoil the ending by telling you what it is. I'm very pleased with the script. When I finished it, I felt that it represented some of the best writing I'd ever done for any television show anywhere, and I thought it could be a better episode than 'The Trouble With Tribbles.' Not as funny. I wanted to do something distinctly different from 'Trouble With Tribbles' and this is it. I turned it in, and went off on the first *Star Trek* cruise and got a telegram from Gene that said, 'Everyone loved your script, have a great cruise.' When I got back I found that the script was not going to be shot. I was told that Gene's lawyer did not like the script and felt that this was not a good episode, and so on his advice, it seems, the script was canceled. That's what I was told by someone who was in a position to know. I don't have any proof in writing, so I have to qualify it by saying someone told me.

"So it was canceled for reasons that had nothing to do with its quality. It was just put on a shelf. I was very hurt and very upset about it, and the only way I can share it is to allow you to buy it and let you decide for yourself if this would have been a good *Star Trek* episode."

Another attempt was made to get "Blood and Fire" on film, but this effort, too, did not reach fruition.

"BLOOD AND ICE"
Rewrite by Herb Wright

The Enterprise is en route to the Copernicus to aid in the annual personnel rotation exchange, which is certainly a mission that provides nothing out of the ordinary – until communication between the two vessels is blanked out. Concern makes its way through the bridge crew, culminating in Data's announcement that he is picking up an automated distress signal from the other ship. A moment or so later the Copernicus is visible on the main viewscreen. All attempts at contact prove futile.

Worf tells Picard that he is picking up life signs, but the readings are providing "odd contradictions." Troi interjects that she can sense numerous life forms, but many of them are growing weaker . . . dying. Then they discover a repulsor field. Is there a battle going on? Against who? Picard calls an emergency meeting in the ready room.

Act One: In the course of the meeting, Troi tries to tap into the Copernicus, and she experiences an incredible sensation of hunger, something she has never really felt before on such a level. Beverly muses that perhaps there is a scarcity of supplies, and that it has resulted in a mutiny, although it is a possibility she doesn't really want to consider.

The Away Team, consisting of Riker, Geordi, Data, Worf, Hodel (now deemed an electrical engineer), Carli (an alien medic of some kind), Tasha, two security guards, Daro and a Romulan named Baldor enter the transporter room. (The latter is of significant interest, suggesting that perhaps at this early stage of the game, Gene Roddenberry and the others involved in the show had considered the idea of having the Romulans be allies of the Federation as well as the Klingons. Thankfully this was ultimately dropped, because the need for a fierce enemy is a tangible

one on the show, and the Ferengi Alliance just doesn't cut it. The Romulans of course did show up in the "Neutral Zone" (no relation to the previously discussed treatment) episode which wrapped up the first season.) They beam over to the Copernicus in a "landing envelope," which essentially provides an atmosphere and habitable living conditions for all contained in it. Data, consulting his tricorder, tells them that the oxygen level in the Copernicus is low, but breathable. They move down the corridor, catch sight of glowing sparkles (essentially the wavicles from the first draft), then they are gone.

Riker contacts the Enterprise, informing them that all is quiet, and requesting that the landing envelope be dropped. This is done, but as soon at it is, they're all sorry that the request was made in the first place. The air stinks, the odor making them think of something that must have died.

"I thought you said we could *breathe* in here, Data," snaps Riker.

"Correct sir."

"How come that damn thing doesn't tell you about the odor of this so-called breathable air?"

A nice, humorous bit, included here just to show some friendly bantering between a couple of the characters that harken back to the original series.

The Away Team is broken into three units, with Tasha leading her people to engineering, Worf to science and Riker to the bridge.

On the Enterprise bridge, Picard informs Beverly that she will be directing the medical aspects of the mission from there, which she agrees with. Turning to her, the captain compassionately notes that she supposedly has a relative on board the Copernicus. After a moment's hesitation, Beverly replies that Robert Crusher, brother of her late husband, serves as the vessel's doctor. Picard tries to be considerate of her feelings in this situation, but she quickly

points out that she has always prepared herself for the worst, although she doesn't want to lose another member of her family. "With Jack gone," she notes, "Robert's all that's left of that part of my life . . . except Wesley, of course.

The captain emphasizes that Jack Crusher would have been proud of his son, which she appreciates, adding that Robert and the boy have never met, but hopefully now they will have the opportunity to do so.

Riker, Data and Baldor enter the bridge of the Copernicus, which is barely lit. Data eventually discovers a body, which the writers describe as "somebody *real* dead . . . empty hollow eyes, sallow skin color and nobody home anymore." Picard, who is monitoring from the Enterprise, asks for identification, and is told by Riker that the man is . . . was . . . the captain of the ship. Data interrupts them with a highly disturbing fact: the man's body contains absolutely no blood.

Act Two: As in the first draft, they discover that all the bridge consoles have been destroyed. It's all very strange and unexplainable to them, particularly Data's latest announcement that the captain's body contains an alien fluid rather than human hemoglobin. Riker tells Picard that it's impossible to download the Copernicus' logs from the bridge, but he'll try from another area. Unfortunately, in checking with Tasha, they discover that engineering is pretty much in the same boat. The same with Worf. Geordi, who is with the Klingon, tells him that he is picking up the infra-red after images of bodies lying on the floor and over chairs, but now everyone who had been in the room is gone. Where the hell have they gone to? Then they see the sparkles again, but, as was the case earlier, they vanish.

Enterprise: Troi is telling Picard that she is still feeling hunger from the Copernicus, as well as fear, anxiety, death, a fight for survival and something that cannot even be described as human. Beverly pipes in that the largest concentration of life form readings are on the lower decks, in medical. This information is conveyed to Riker. Data once again serves as an interruption, lifting up the dead man's hand to show it to Riker, and watching in amazement as the limb begins to twitch. Riker is stunned, even after the twitching has stopped. Then, the dead captain is up, his arms wrapping themselves tightly around Riker's neck. Data manages to throw the corpse clear, but it manages to claw the neck of a security officer (or red shirt, as they used to be known on the old show), before collapsing. The captain gets to his lifeless feet and starts towards Riker again. The commander fires his phaser, which sends the corpse back to the deck. Seconds later, he is up again, moving in for the kill. The security guard sets his phaser for kill and fires. The body disappears, leaving a cloud of sparkles in its aftermath, which those people standing there breathe in to their lungs. The three of them, choking, move off of the bridge.

In engineering, Hodel has climbed inside a console and is attempting to do some repair work, when he feels a tugging on his leg, and is viciously yanked out of frame with such force, that some wires are actually ripped from the console. Tasha and Daro respond to the man's screams, while Riker, Data and Baldor start running to the area, as does Worf. Baldor, however, goes off on his own and disappears. Elsewhere, what is obviously another dead crewmember, claws Hodel's face and is moving in for the kill, when the man fires his phaser. The body disappears, leaving sparkles which envelope the man, who slips into unconsciousness.

Act Three: The Away Team stands above Hodel's unconscious form, studying the claw marks on his face. Carli suggests that the man be beamed back to Enterprise sickbay, but Beverly disagrees, telling Picard

that they're not even sure what infected the Copernicus crew, and without further information, Hodel may bring whatever it is to them. Picard suggests that they place him into "total isolation, full sano-lock, and 60 day observation." Beverly agrees with this idea, and Hodel is beamed "home." But as he does so, an exterior view of the vessels shows sparkles of a different sort transversing the distance between them. Hodel rematerializes in the isolation bay of sickbay, where he scratches an itch before his hands go limp again. After some study, Beverly has to admit that she can't explain whatever it is that's affecting Hodel, pointing out that it's neither a virus nor bacterial. One thing she does know is that whatever they're dealing with, has become intricately connected with his hemoglobin, which is rapidly replaced by the alien fluid Data had discovered earlier. Once the process is complete, all the victim can hope for is death.

On the Copernicus, the remnants of the Away Team make their way to medical, when their communicators pick up the sound of Baldor's frequency. They reach medical, see a cloud of sparkles, but continue. Once inside, they are horrified by what they discover: the place is in a shambles, blood gone from containers, but no bodies. Geordi adds that he is detecting thermal readings which indicate that people were in this area a short while earlier. They move further into sickbay, where they finally come across a group of men and women, obviously dead, their fingers covered in blood. Seeing these living humans, the bloody group get to their feet and start advancing towards them. Naturally, the Away Team retreats, and as they do so Worf lets out a horrified scream when he catches sight of the bloody remains of Baldor. They move quickly through sickbay. Worf fires his phaser at one of them, and the body disappears, leaving sparkles in its wake. The zombies, as they are

called by the writers, continue pursuing our people. Things get pretty intense as they barely make their way into medical and seal the doors behind them. Riker contacts the Enterprise, asking Picard to beam them out of there. The captain's reply is that he can't.

Act Four: After conducting numerous tests, Beverly tells Picard that they are dealing with Regulan bloodworms, an announcement which stuns the captain who wants to know why, when the bloodworms have completed eating the blood of its victim's body, that person simply doesn't die. She replies that someone, in an effort to create an ultimate doomsday weapon, added a genetic alteration that destroyed the mind of its host, and replaced it with its own thought impulses, which are deemed "a little awkward at first, but workable." Picard wants to know how they can cure their people. Beverly has an idea, but isn't sure that there's enough time to carry it out. It is her estimation that the Away Team will have about two hours before the bloodworms take effect.

Back on the Copernicus, the zombies are doing their best to get through the door separating them from the Away Team, but so far they're having little luck. Unfortunately, all of them have begun to itch terribly, which is the first symptom of the disease. Data, the only one not affected by this, states that the ship's logs seem to indicate that the Copernicus broke a seven hundred year old quarantine by entering the Regulan system. The conversation is interrupted by the silence that suddenly greets them. Where have the zombies gone? They can not ponder this question for long, however, as Carli screams out, the worms moving under his arm and causing the alien to cry out. He eventually passes out, and Data states that he has no idea what they can give him to ease the pain. Worf is the first to voice the realization that Carli is becoming one of "them." Riker contacts Picard, asking that they be beamed within the repulsor field. The zombies then break through the doors and are nearly upon them, when the transporter beam pulls them away.

Beverly comes to the Enterprise bridge with the cure. Picard says they'll beam it over, but she insists on going herself. On a monitor screen she shows that she has created an anti-bloodworm, which devours the bloodworms themselves. Both of them realize that the cure is probably more dangerous than the plague. She explains that the idea came from Wesley who told her of an old Earth game called Pac-Man (*puh-lease* – spare me). To stop the anti-worms from getting out of control, a poison is then administered to the victim, which is harmless to the host but kills the anti-worms. Beverly feels that she is the only one qualified to handle the administration of this cure. Just then, the turbo lift doors open, admitting the newly zombietized Hodel.

Act Five: Beverly quickly explains that it was too late to save Hodel, but if they phaser him, the disease will be spread throughout the Enterprise. Picard contacts the transporter room and has Hodel beamed back to the Copernicus.

In the cargo bay of that ship, the Away Team have appeared in the midst of the repulsor field, where they find ten frozen crewmembers, as well as Doctor Robert Crusher, an officer named Yarell (not the same character as the first draft) and an "ugly" alien named Rohan. Outside the perimeter of the field, the zombies are trying to get in. Riker questions Crusher on what happened, but Yarell interjects that Rohan was responsible for piloting the ship into Regulan space. Crusher identifies the two of them, and indicates the frozen bodies as all that's left of the Copernicus crew, with the exception, of course, of the zombies. He offers to freeze Carli, which is a process that will, if nothing else, slow down the

spread of the worms until they can come up with a more permanent cure. Geordi adds that it really is becoming a matter of time, because the repulsor field is weakening.

Wesley comes on to the Enterprise bridge, telling Picard that he believes the Copernicus may actually explode because of the amount of energy that the repulsor field has been drawing from the anti-matter containment tank. That element could . . . and probably will . . . come into contact with matter, resulting in a cataclysmic explosion. And, he adds, if the Copernicus is destroyed, so is the Enterprise, and all of this will take place within five minutes. Beverly contacts the captain, saying that she's ready to beam over. He tells her the situation and their new schedule. Anyone not cured within the time frame must remain behind. Understanding this, she beams over.

Once appearing in the repulsor field, there is a *very* brief reunion between Beverly and Robert Crusher as she starts to administer the cure. Yarell protests that Rohan shouldn't be saved, because it was his intention to spread the bloodworms throughout Federation space. Rohan merely says that he is proud to die with so many of his enemies. Yarell (in an ironic reversal of the first draft) pulls a phaser on the alien, and Riker has to talk him out of firing. Beverly continues what she's doing, and Rohan manages to steal Worf's phaser, which he waves at the humans. Worf, having had enough, whips the phaser out of the alien's hand, grabs him by the throat, lifts him in the air and as the repulsor field goes down for good, he throws the alien's body into the horde of zombies, who instantly start to devour him. Sparkles fill the air as the Away Team and the others, now fully cured, are beamed back to the Enterprise, which departs the area right before the Copernicus explodes.

* * *

Whoa! What a hell of an ending. Worf

throwing an alien to certain death at the hands of the zombies? Jeez!

As can be clearly discerned, this version of "Blood and Fire" was drastically different than the original. Gone, for the most part, is the AIDS allegory, and in its place is a straight-out tale of horror that reads like *Star Trek Meets Night of the Living Dead.* And yet while the changes are many, it doesn't take away from the fact that this is one hell of a suspenseful and scary teleplay. The idea of using Robert Crusher really doesn't serve much of a purpose, but outside of that, just about everything is handled with great logic.

Explains writer Herb Wright, who served as producer of *Next Generation's* first and fifth seasons, "When I first came on the show I, frankly, hadn't see much of *Star Trek* other than the movies and five or six episodes from the first *Star Trek* series. One of the things I did immediately was go back and look at as many of the old shows as possible. What I found was such an enormous variety of kinds of shows. They weren't all about social themes, they weren't all about personal stories. A lot of them were action adventure, a lot of them were suspense, a lot of them were really farces. I figured there was room in the mix for *Night of the Living Dead,* zombies in space.

"When I came back during fifth season, I read the script again because they were hardup for stories and I brought it in. I mentioned it to [Co-Executive Producer] Michael Piller and he said, 'What was it?' because he thought he had read everything when he came in. I said, 'You probably never saw this draft. If anything, you probably read 'Blood and Fire,' and this one was called 'Blood and Ice.' I printed it out and brought it in. The staff loved it, Rick loved it, but Piller said, 'Nice script, but it's really a first season type of show.' Oh well."

"SEE SPOT RUN"
Written by Michael Halperin

Proceeding to Procyon III, the Enterprise is searching for a supposed lost colony, a group of "high-tech iconoclasts" who settled that particular world. When the world had first been discovered, the dominant form of life was an animal known as the Rookas, a panda-like race who were not aggressive by nature, and were nearly made extinct by the settlers. Those that did survive, were taught to do various tasks, much like chimpanzees are on Earth today, and the species is bred on farms situated throughout the world.

An Away Team led by Riker, and including Wesley, beam down to one of the aforementioned farms, where they encounter a fifteen year old girl (Delva) who is obviously frightened by something. She waves what is essentially a 20th Century shotgun at them. Naturally they are able to disarm her, and eventually learn that her parents have gone into a town area to partake in an annual celebration. Wesley is left behind with Delva as they proceed.

Picard tries to contact the Away Team, but discovers that somehow the transporter engaged a device set up by the colonists which has blocked off all communication, and cut off the automatic beacon they had been detecting as well.

Once they arrive in town, the Away Team is surprised to see that the settlers have reverted to a more simple lifestyle. They live in wooden buildings which supplant the ruins of the nearby buildings. In addition, there are a variety of book stalls in the main square and everyone gets around via horse and carriage. Then they take note of a being known as a Memory Master, who begins detailing the history of this world, which somehow manages to combine and twist the history of both the planet and the Federation. Once this little oration is complete, the people start throwing their books into a fire. Riker manages to retrieve one of them, and is shocked to find that all of the pages are blank. Then, an old man named Kort takes the book from his hands, throws it into the flames and leads them to his home.

Meanwhile, Delva is giving Wes some history concerning Procyon III, telling him that there was a time when the society flourished with technology, but then the planet was almost destroyed by the misuse of the same technology. So the people revolted against men of knowledge, and illiteracy is now the norm. It is deemed better to be illiterate, than to have the potential to destroy their world. She does, however, have one book, which features the infamous Dick and Jane.

Back with the Away Team, Kort has basically explained the same thing that Delva did, and adds that real books are kept hidden, because they are highly illegal to have. History is taught to the population by the Memory Masters, so that some basic working knowledge will be passed from one generation to the next. At that moment, the door bursts open and the equivalent of police enter, capturing Troi, Geordi and Kort, while Riker, Data and Tasha manage to escape. They attempt to contact the Enterprise, but to no avail.

According to the outline, Wesley accidentally forgets about the Prime Directive (let's face it, love him or hate him, Wesley would *not* forget that directive) and reads from a Robert Frost book of poetry he just happens to carry with him. While Delva is frightened by the fact he is actually reading, she manages to find some solace in the words that are being spoken. Shortly thereafter, the girl's parents return, are told that Wesley is a friend, and go on to explain that some strangers are being tried for treason. When they are alone, Wes tries to get Delva to assist him in rescuing the others.

While hiding in what's left of a scientific complex, Riker accidentally falls to a lower level, where he sees a Rooka tending to books. Then he comes to the realization that these creatures are actually intelligent, and they learned to write, read and speak from being associated with the colonists. Naturally they fear if such knowledge became public, they would be exterminated, so they keep these abilities a secret from the humans, while at the same time are drawn to making sure the library survives.

At their trial, Troi, Geordi and Kort are sentenced to death, with the Memory Master using a twisted version of a Federation doctrine as the reason.

The Rookas help Riker to obtain some "primitive weapons," and they're used to get the others out of jail. Wes and Delva catch up to them, while Riker uses the Memory Master as a hostage, and tells them that if the Away Team isn't given back their weapons and communicators, then Troi will wipe out the history of the planet from the Memory Master's mind. Kort steps forward with an old book of Federation codes, which the elderly Rooka reads from, including a call for "freedom of expression; freedom of worship; freedom of assembly." The people actually take these words to heart and turn against the Tribunal, calling for justice for everyone.

Picard manages to get through to the Away Team and beams them back up, and while the captain reports their findings to the Federation, the elderly Rooka is sitting in a field on the planet, reading "Run, Spot, Run," to some children, who slowly repeat his words.

* * *

While this story would have certainly

needed a lot of work to flesh it out, it does present some interesting concepts, most notable among them being a society that has forced itself to become illiterate so that it can save itself from the potential disaster of having too much knowledge, without the wisdom to use it properly. The ending does, however, seems contrived, and actually harkens back to "The Omega Glory" episode of the original show, where Captain James T. Kirk reads from the Constitution of the United States in an effort to unite the Yangs and the Kohms.

"THE LEGACY"
Written by Paul Aratow

Eeryone on the bridge of the Enterprise is surprised to be picking up a radio broadcast of music. This is interrupted by an emergency signal from a passenger ship which is supposedly in a "Bermuda Triangle of space." The starship approaches, but is unable to grab the vessel with its tractor beam because of an ion storm. A woman pilot named Lara volunteers to take a shuttle to the ship, which Picard allows. Unfortunately, she disappear in the storm and scanners indicate that there is no other ship in the vicinity.

Shortly thereafter, she mysteriously returns and is debriefed by the captain. Lara reluctantly tells him that she had seen a beautiful winged creature outside of the shuttle. She is then examined by Beverly Crusher, who deems her to be in perfect health. The mystery deepens when the Enterprise begins sending out its own distress signal, and the crew learns that two other Federation vessels are now en route to rescue them.

The ship starts picking up the strange music that had appeared earlier, and it seems to be taking control of Lara. All communication channels are suddenly jammed, and there is no way to alert the Federation or the two approaching vessels of the danger that exists there. Then, Beverly's further examinations of Lara determines that she is pregnant with a rapidly growing fetus. This was not the case before she went out in the shuttle.

As the child inside her develops, Lara grows stronger and "displays extraordinary powers," which leads Beverly to the conclusion that the child is super human. The jamming of subspace communication lessens to the point where Picard is able to contact Starfleet, which replies that they may order an abortion. Lara, thanks to the child, picks up signals from the broadcast they're intercepting, and warns Picard that the Enterprise is in grave danger, which can only be averted by changing the course of the starship. Picard refuses, probably trying to determine whether it's Lara or the alien threat speaking, but the woman somehow manages to convince the navigator to follow through on her warning, and

the course is changed, resulting in their missing disaster.

Picard is given the order to destroy the embryo, but he manages to come up with a reason not to do so at that time. Meanwhile, Lara tells the captain that in a parallel universe there is a battle between good and evil going on, and the good alien is attempting to come into this universe to battle the evil. The child is the key, and she wants the two of them to take a shuttlecraft. Finally, Picard "realizes that only Lara can make the decision about her future. That's the true meaning of the Prime Directive. Lara elects to go where no woman has gone before by having the child."

As the story comes to an end, Lara takes the shuttlecraft and heads for the signal they had been picking up, as well as her destiny.

* * *

Again, a story which would have probably turned out to be a decent one if it had been fleshed out. The idea of a rapidly developing child made it to the air in season two's "The Child."

"FERENGI GOLD"
Written by Gene Roddenberry

Gene Roddenberry began what was his last effort for *Star Trek* with a bit of background, explaining that the intent of "Ferengi Gold" was to comment on the fact that the Enterprise has risen above 20th Century greed. "*Star Trek's* people value personal challenge and satisfaction above materiality," he said, "and our story comments on the difference between them and the super-capitalistic little Ferengi aliens. Plus, we also hope to tap the 'Wheel of Fortune' fascination of our television audience, i.e. its affection for prizes and displays of valuables ... Last but not least, this is also about *sex*. Our story is about sex *and* gold."

As though this were something new to *Star Trek*, the bridge crew of the Enterprise is abuzz with the rumor that this particular star cluster they're in contains a world that has developed on a parallel course to Earth. The vessel approaches Lerta-117. Dr. Kate Pulaski (this story was obviously written for season two) comes to the bridge, establishing herself as something of a historian who has never seen a parallel world before. According to Data, a populated area on Lerta bears many similarities to Boston in the 1770s. Picard wishes that it mirrored France at that time, for it would have been Earth's first experience with political freedom. Pulaski counters that North America was first and considerably more interesting. Data quells the debate by noting that so-called parallel worlds are only similar to each other rather than identical.

Enterprise draws closer, and more accurate readings reveal that the culture mirrors North America in the 18th Century. Riker wants to lead an Away Team but Picard is reluctant to possibly interfere. Worf abruptly announces that a Ferengi cargo ship is locked in a lower orbit and has not yet detected Enterprise. Picard has

the starship put in a parking orbit on the opposite side so that the planet will lie between the two ships.

Due to the presence of the Ferengi, Picard authorizes Riker to take an Away Team down to the surface. Riker, Troi and Geordi (wouldn't his visor draw unwanted attention?) beam down in the appropriate clothing. They're able to blend in, though two things come to mind as they observe this world: "The female members of this planet are unusually lovely — tall, fair-skinned beauties." Also, the people wear a great amount of gold jewelry. At least now they can understand why the Ferengi are so interested in this world.

To question the natives, Riker has a tricorder beamed down. Pretending to be a stage actor and magician, he "does an excellent job of double-talking about 'lights and shadow and images,'" but ultimately it turns out that the locals don't recognize either the Ferengi or their cargo vessel. It's suggested that Riker perform his magic for their spiritual leader, the Reverend Mathis Fergreson. The Away Team is led to a *motorbus* (highlighting one of the differences between this world and earth of this era), which takes them away.

They arrive at the Commons Church and meet Reverend Fergreson. Roddenberry noted, "Religion here is similar with differences from Christian religon ... As for Fergreson, think of Jerry Falwell but in a situation of far more power and respect than Falwell is permitted." Riker shows him the tricorder images and Fergreson responds that "it's the Angels of Beotane (God)," and these people must be holy ones to hold such images. The Reverend had been told by the "angels" not to mention them except to the most trusted leaders. These angels, he adds, are far to the west.

Noting the Reverend's gold bracelet, Riker asks if the angels are interested in the substance. "Of course," is the response. "It is Holy metal, beloved of Beotane and His

Angels. From it they receive their strength and purity."

Picard has the Away Team beamed back aboard. In the transporter room, he explains that sensors indicate gold is about as abundant here as it was on Earth, but it is found in rich vein concentrates, making it quite simple to mine. It is the captain's determination that the Ferengi, their greed be damned, not interfere with the evolution of this world. This parallel society could potentially be important for Federation scholars, but contamination must be minimized. The best move would probably be to send the Away Team to the location of Ferengi transporter activity. Riker starts to assemble his people when Picard (in a silly, childish and out of character moment) "bribes" Pulaski into agreeing with him that Riker is fatigued and, due to regulations, must stay aboard. Riker objects but is effectively overrruled. Ultimately Picard, Pulaski, Troi and Data beam down.

They appear in the vicinity of a mining location and immediately notice several "tattered" natives who exhausitvely work the mine. On one of the native's wrists is an odd-looking bracelet. One Ferengi with an electronic whip weapon (as seen in "The Last Outpost") watches over them. Lots of gold is in evidence. At that moment, the Away Team is ambushed and rendered unconscious.

In the mine it becomes apparent that the natives being brought in are females, and the Ferengi are delighted that they captured two more (Pulaski and Troi). According to the treatment, "They bring Troi and Pulaski back to consciousness first — followed by not a little lascivious pinching and prodding, expressions of delight at their firm bodies. What we're seeing is a side of the Ferengi only hinted at previously ... Like Earth's 'robber barons' of long ago, the Ferengi relate to females as *objects*, mindless possessions, and treat them accordingly ... Gold is only part of their interest on this simple little world. To these big-eared little aliens, females are something to be controlled by waving shiny baubles under their noses or by easily deceiving them with promises. Sexual equality is considered ridiculous."

When they awaken, Picard and Data are wearing the bracelets they noticed earlier, which are actually agony devices activated whenever the Ferengi are displeased with them (shades of "Gamesters of Triskellion"). We alternate between threats to the Away Team and an ongoing discussion of how horny the Ferengis are and how this planet represents a true paradise to them beyond just gold.

At first Pulaski and Troi are totally uncooperative with their Ferengi "hosts," but change their attitude when they are told they will be beamed aboard the cargo vessel for distribution at the ship's next stop. Meanwhile, Picard and Data are forced to stack gold ingots but their identity is revealed when Picard's hidden communicator falls to the ground. Realizing that it's up to them, "Troi and Pulaski come on to the Ferengi with every trick they've learned in their space travels ... [They] know how to be super-seductive." Their intent is to delay the Ferengi from killing Picard and Data while simlutaneously convincing the Ferengi to drop their guard, which

gives the duo the opportunity to gain the upper hand. Troi and Pulaski free Picard and Data and the four of them beam back to the Enterprise.

Picard is described as being angrier than we've ever seen him because of the Ferengi plan to utilize the world below them as a forced labor slave-camp as well as their treatment of the native women. Picard considers it the equivalent of rape. He develops a plan which will cause the Ferengi to have to abandon their hope of kidnapping native women because, if all works out, "they won't have the room." He then gives the order for Enterprise to be revealed to the cargo ship. Phasers and photon torpedoes are armed. "Surprised by the unexpected appearance of a Federation heavy cruiser, shocked by its menacing readiness, the Ferengi captain is only too happy to accept Picard's invitation to beam aboard for a meeting."

During that meeting, Picard notes that the Ferengi have as much right to be here as the Federation, but since this world holds such a historical interest to the Federation, the hope is that it would be allowed to evolve naturally. To this end, he claims, the Federation will purchase any rights that the Ferengi may have. As a result, Picard has ton after ton of gold patterned from energy by the Enterprise transporters beamed over to the cargo ship. The vessel departs with every available inch loaded with the

gold. On the planet there is confirmation that the prisoners have been released.

"For those who may not understand the mechanics of a 'robber baron' society," Roddenberry noted, "Picard points out that what they've done is to seriously disrupt the Ferengi economy. The value of gold to them was based on its scarcity." Even if this bullion doesn't flood the market, it will probably cause the government to ban visits to planets where gold can be found so readily. Data comments on the more positive aspects of gold, and Picard responds that if the Ferengi can learn from this treasure to appreciate the artistic loveliness of gold, "this might accomplish more than even wrecking their economy."

* * *

Not one of the best from the pen of Gene Roddenberry. The story really seems rather pointless and doesn't represent much of a morality tale. What's the gist? Appreciate gold for more than its fiscal worth, or be smallminded the rest of your life? Don't steal what doesn't belong to you? Overall "Ferengi Gold" just doesn't work, and it's not surprising that it wasn't taken any further, although there was rumor for a time that *Next Generation*'s Tracy Torme was going to attempt to expand the treatment into a teleplay.

"GENIUS IS PAIN"
Written by Tracy Torme

The Enterprise makes preparations to beam aboard four members of the Davalii, a race essentially recognized as the tortured geniuses of the glaxy.

"Their entire planet," writes Tracy Torme, "is made up of twisted artists, suffering artists, depressed artists and crazy artists." At the same time, they are geniuses in mathematics, though they hate calculus. The Davalii are also impressed with earthlings, particularly our numerical systems. "In a stunning stroke of non-logic, all Davalii are now named with the numbers one to twenty-six. Why stop at twenty six? The Davalii shrug, 'Why not?' Thus their planet is filled with millions of ones, twos, threes, etc. Somehow, they manage to tell each other apart."

Due to the fact that they believe earthlings are bohemian by nature and force themselves to live rigid lives filled with responsibility, they take an enormous amount of pleasure in trying to tempt humans with enjoyable things. To this end, the Davalii take it as a sacred duty to constantly tempt the crew, urging them to drop what they're doing and have some fun.

The Davalii philosophy is basically to do your own thing, any time, any place. If you feel like spray painting a wall, go ahead. Never eat an eraser? Now's the time to try. If someone's walking by, sticking out your foot can cause hilarious results. And above all, there is no higher commitment than the devotion of art. Art comes first at all times.

To the Davalii, reacting negatively to a prank, or trying to restrict what another feels like doing, is the height of poor taste and bad manners. Picard is warned by Starfleet not to put any major controls on these free spirits. The captain and crew will just have to grin and bear it until they reach their destination, which is New Montana. There these artists are to design a memorial to the hundreds that have died trying to tame this world.

The four Davalii are beamed aboard. Nine is tall and gangly, a practical joker, totally erratic and unpredictable. Seven is a manic depressive who sees everything in black and white (mostly black). Thirteen is a female who has a severe case of the giggles every time Picard speaks. Twenty is short, fat and uncooperative. He refuses to leave the transporter. Picard decides to let him be for the time being, although the intention would have been to cut back to him throughout the episode, watching Twenty standing on the platform, refusing to budge.

The Davalii begin to wreak good-natured havoc all over the ship: painting the walls, pulling pranks, playing horrid, wild sounding music, and adding "mood lighting" to the hallways.

Thirteen disrupts Wesley's lessons – school is such a drag, she complains. Why not go out and play? The kids love her but the teacher is not amused.

Nine causes chaos in a shipboard restaurant – pulling chairs out from under people, pouring salt on their food when they're not looking and wolfing down his food in a disgusting manner just to get a reaction.

Seven has fallen into a deep depression over his sudden unrequited love for Deanna Troi. He follows her around, writing flowery love letters and begging her to join him in reckless passion. Deanna is flustered, but Riker is thoroughly enjoying this, egging her on mischievously. Seven grows more and more melancholy, finally threatening to cut off his ear if she leaves his love unrequited. Fortunately, she talks him out of this drastic step. His relentless adoration nonetheless continues.

Data is fascinated and enthralled by the Davalii's antics. He is becoming influenced by them and his personality is becoming a bit too zany for the captain's liking. Still, Data can't seem to get enough of the Davalii.

Not so for Captain Picard, who is growing increasingly concerned over the effect the visitors are having on his crew. Discipline is becoming a problem and Picard is helpless to put an end to it. Finally, when Nine gets into the enviornmental control system and causes it to snow on the bridge, Picard has had enough. He finds all three Davalii (Twenty remains in the transporter room) huddled in a room. They are "globing": tossing a small, lit globe to one another. The globe grows brighter as it's passed from hand to hand; it seems to exaggerate the mood of its handler shortly after contact. Eventually, they all sit together in a circle, lightly touching the beachball-sized globe. They ask Picard to join in but he politely declines, while informing them that they're within eight hours of New Montana. Finding that they've done nothing in regard to the ceremonial artwork they've been commissioned to create, Picard urges them to do so, figuring this will at least keep them occupied.

He starts a discussion of the trials and hardships the pioneers of New Montana faced in forging a home for themselves. This seems to spark little interest. However, when he mentions the glory they will receive upon completion of their project, they get cracking. As Picard leaves, they are already bickering over what kind of design to create.

Back on the bridge, the Prime Minister of New Montana appears on the screen with his prim and proper wife. They are delighted to greet the Enterprise. The upcoming dedication means so much to the residents of New Montana.

When the Davalii finally reveal their creation to the Enterprise officers, they are shocked. The sculpture is in extremely poor taste (a humorous portrayal of pioneers dying around a campfire). Despite protest from the crew, the Davalii are brazenly certain that their statue will be well received. They eagerly anticipate the glorious response they will be accorded in New Montana.

Knowing this will cause an ugly interplanetary incident, Picard takes a bold step. Data is secretly commissioned to rework the sculpture: Worf, Riker, Wes and Geordi pitch in with ideas, which Data implements at super-human speed. Ultimately, the pioneer characters are transformed from pathetic and humorous to bold and courageous. The sculpture is once again covered with a canvas and transported down to the planet before the Davalii can get a look at it. Picard breathes a sigh of relief when the Davalii are at last beamed down as well. Still, he's quite worried about what he predicts to be their violent reaction to Data's reworking of their art.

Back on the bridge, word comes up from the Prime Minister of New Montana that the piece is a raging success (inhabitants can be heard cheering in the background). Nine comes on screen, delighted with the "practical joke" the crew of the Enterprise has played on the Davalii. "You're learning," says Thirteen.

Picard prepares to beam the Davalii aboard for the return journey, but the Prime Minister intervenes. He has invited "these charming people" to stay on New Montana until the next ship arrives (over two months from now). Picard tries to give the New Montanans a subtle warning, but they are too enthralled with the Davalii to notice.

While saying goodbye to the Enterprise, the Prime Minister gets a pie in the face from Nine (as a way of saying thanks for everything). He laughs it off good-naturedly, commenting on what a bunch of

delightful cut-ups these Davalii are. As the Enterprise breaks out of orbit, Picard wonders if he'll still feel that way a day from now.

* * *

As Tracy Torme developed this storyline, he came up with the notion of former Monty Pythoner John Cleese being cast in the role of Nine, which led to the offshoot idea that Nine would refuse to talk to anyone who did not have a number for a name. When Picard suggested something to Riker, adding, "Make it so, Number One," Nine began babbling, introducing himself and the other members of the Davalii. What could have been a truly funny episode was shot down by the show's producers, particularly the notion of using Cleese. Ironic that a short time later they would feature Joe Piscopo in the extremely *unfunny* episode, "The Outrageous Okona."

"I.Q. TEST"
Written by Herb Wright

Teaser: There has been a shuttle crash on an alien planet, with Data and Geordi hanging on for dear life over a chasm. Riker is on the planet, too, but separated from them. As all this is going on, there is a star flare and Q appears, "angelically dressed in a long white robe." Q peers over the cliff's edge and starts to laugh as he gestures theatrically over the chasm. He is thrilled at watching the human spirit at work.

At that moment, there is another flare and Q-Too appears, "as a woman, tightly clad in black alien leathers. A raven-haired ball of fire, who glances imperiously over the edge," unimpressed. In the ensuing discussion, Q continues to sing the praises of humanity, which Q-Too could obviously give two dips about. Then Riker approaches Geordi and Data. Using an almost super-human effort, he pulls them to safety. Q is delighted, Q-Too remains unmoved. The Away Team manages to beam back aboard the Enterprise.

Act One: Picard's log informs us that the Enterprise lost a shuttle in its ongoing rescue attempt of the missing colony on Xlapak Three, though they were able to save the Away Team. Another attempt must be made.

While Geordi is in engineering attempting to figure out what the next move should be from his point of view, Q and Q-Too materialize, continuing their conversation from before. Q proclaims, "You dare to call a species which could produce the marvels that surround you, stupid? Look at this, will you! Why, they have harnessed the fusion power of a small star inside there!"

"How charming," she replies. "And oh so primitive. Really, Q, do you dare to gamble on these apes?"

"Absolutely. They're my apes and I love them. Let me show you more."

Cutting to the bridge, Picard is getting communique's from all over the ship regarding the appearance of Q and his companion. Frustrated, Picard growls, "Damn that Q. Why is it that every bloody time we find ourselves in the thick of a critical mission, Q shows up! Why the hell does Q pick moments like this?"

"Because, Captain," responds Q, "this is exactly when you humans are so interesting."

Within moments, Picard is stunned to discover that the Enterprise crew is part of a bet being waged between the two Qs; an Olympics of sorts between humans and the Zaa-Narr, a brilliant yet savage race. Q-Too announces the stakes: she will annihilate the losing team along with their entire species everywhere throughout the galaxy. Picard protests.

Q: "That's ludicrous, Q-Too. I will not do that . . . I like my human beings. Besides, the galaxy would be a lonelier place without them."

She reduces the wages to just the Enterprise crew and then goads Q on with the fact that if he doesn't accept, she'll go back to the Continuum and spread the news that Q has "gone native." This does the trick, as he announces that they accept her terms.

Instantly, another starshp appears, "flopping" into position alongside the Enterprise. "It looks like an ominous alien version of the Stealth bomber," Wright explains, "angular, muscular and lethal in its design."

Q's team will consist of Picard, Riker and Crusher. Q-Too materializes her players, Aa'Tina (executioner, as there is no need for doctors), First Officer Baa'Lum and Captain Chac-'Maal. Picard tries to make nice-nice, but the aliens will have none of it, laughing off his attempts at friendship.

Act Two: The Qs start debating each other again. Picard wants to know what the point of this whole thing is, but he's ignored. Riker adds that if they're going to play some games, shouldn't they at least be aware of the rules? No rules, says Q-Too. Each event will dictate its own guidelines, and high score wins. Losers all die. Argues Picard, "Our lives are not like poker chips, to be thrown away in some silly game!" Q, annoyed at the taunting of Q-Too, dismisses this notion by turning the entire bridge crew into a series of poker chips, "Geordi, Troi and Worf's faces, all trapped as holograms inside the big chips, slowly moving in silent agony. The outside chip rim reads: U.S.S. Enterprise Casino." Q-Too does the same to crewmembers of the Zaa-Naar ship, resulting in Chac-'Maal proclaiming, "We are nothing before you, oh Q!" Q-Too is elated while Q is turned off at "that vulgar sort of display of frightened affection."

Ever the diplomat, Picard approaches Chac'Maal with the intention of settling the situation. The alien captain will have none of it. There will be only one way that the situation be settled, and with that everyone vanishes. An instant later, Picard and Chac'Maal stand at two sides of a triangular ring, which is lit from above. Both of them are stripped to boxer-like trunks, accompanied by spiked gloves and ring shoes. Q-Too is at the bell corner while Q, wearing a tux, serves as emcee. Riker and Beverly flank Picard's corner, while the two aliens flank the opposing captain.

Once again, Picard refuses to fight until he's told that if he doesn't, he'll serve as Chac'Maal's lunch. "I'll eat your brains first," snarls the alien. Picard finally agrees, provided that they fight without the spikes on their gloves. The fight begins, Chac'Maal connecting with every kick and punch he throws out, but Picard's return punches passing through the alien as though he wasn't there. It turns out that it has to do with a series of circles which are also in the ring. Red circles make someone transparent and white ones make them whole again. Using this information, Picard is able to gain the upper hand, which immediately causes the two Qs to start fighting again, actually resulting in Chac'Maal being declared the winner of the round.

Q gets to choose the next game, and everyone finds themselves around a card table. "Cards," offers Q. "A game of chance." All the chips appear, Picard's eyes locking on the one featuring a pained Troi.

Act Three: A game of poker – accompanied by a bit of Q hocus pocus and commentary – ensues. Riker and Picard flirt with Q-Too in an effort to win some favor from her. Meanwhile, as had been established earlier, Chac'Maal is holding a royal flush while Riker's cards are garbage. However, this does not stop the commander from performing one of the biggest bluffs of his career. Eventually it comes time for the cards to be revealed, and Riker displays the royal flush, with Chac'Maal's hand now being what had been in Riker's. The alien is furious, but Q disputes the claim that he cheated. "Dealer's choice," he says simply. "And in my game of poker, a good bluff always wins. Match to Riker."

Picard stuns just about everyone by separating the Zaa-Narr crew chips he just acquired and shoving them back toward Chac'Maal. "We will always do the honorable thing, Captain Chac'Maal," he notes.

Now it is Q-Too's turn to pick an event, and her first suggestion is a five kilometer swim through shark-infested waters, "sprinkled lighting with piranha." Picard has Q call for a time-out. Suddenly they're in Ten-Forward at banquet tables. The Zaa-Narr wait for Q-Too to give them a blessing and then they rip hungrily into their lunch, the sounds reverbrating through the room.

"What does that sound like to you, Number One?" muses Picard.

"A Klingon picnic?"

"Exactly. Maybe a little Klingon psychology might go far here."

Picard approaches the Zaa-Narr table with a bottle of wine, offering a toast to Chac'Maal's coming death. Leaping to his feet and raising his goblet, Chac'Maal counters that he'll drink to Picard's death. Then Picard offers his pity for a race that has allowed itself to be used like dogs by Q-Too. Chac'Maal rejects his pity, which, Picard says, might be the situation someday when the mistress rejects her slave. Before the alien can respond, everyone is gone again, this time appearing in a shuttle. Q has managed to convince Q-Too to alter her plans for the next game. Instead, they will partake in a shuttle race.

Act Four: Things are made more complicated by the fact that they're supposed to navigate the shuttles through an asteroid belt, sans controls. At Picard's fury, Q comments, "Of course you do know I'd never allow you not to be in control, Captain." In other words, there are controls – they just have to find them. As the shuttle is rocked by asteroids, Picard and Riker get more desperate. Q is then wearing a Hawaiian shirt, shades and baggie shorts, noting, "If you know how to hang ten, you'll become one with the wave."

Beverly makes the connection to surfing, explaining that "that's how they ride the crest of our home planet's ocean waves."

As foolish as they feel doing it, Picard and Riker move behind their chairs and mimic a surfing position offered by Q. As a result, the flight smoothes out, Picard exclaiming, "*We are the controls!*" Through this method they maneuver the shuttle safely through that turbulent quadrant of space. By thinking warp one, the shuttle abruptly achieves that speed, passing the Zaa-Narr shuttle, but it's only a short matter of time before they catch up.

Both shuttles achieve warp two, "headed toward a huge, pulsing red triangle which hovers in space, beyond the glowing asteroid course guides." The Zaa-Narr pull ahead, but

Q decides to slow them down with an asteroid suddenly appearing before the aliens. When it becomes obvious that the other shuttle will be destroyed by the asteroid, Picard tells Riker to change course for interception. The shuttle "rams" the Zaa-Narr shuttle from the rear, successfully knocking it out of the way of the asteroid, while simultaneoulsy pushing that ship through the red triangle.

Everyone is back in Ten-Forward, Q-Too celebrating their latest victory. Picard tries to explain his motivation for saving the aliens, but Q is too indignant to really hear him. The Zaa-Narr have a score of 78 while the humans have only 20.

"That's why I'll tell you a little story about another being I once knew," says Q, "who made me promise on his deathbed, that when things got rough, I'd ask you to go back out there and win just one for the Great Bird of the . . ."

Q-Too interrupts, ready for the next event. Naturally another argument erupts between them, giving Chac'Maal the opportunity to ask Picard what kind of warrior he is. The captain responds, "A peaceful warrior, I would hope," but the alien tells him not to expect the same from him. Why not? Picard wonders. Perhaps he might like it. There's no time to consider that thought as the Qs stop arguing and everyone finds themselves on the Enterprise bridge, only now it has been redesigned as a game show set.

"Fact or fiction," announces Q. "Stay tuned, we'll be right back."

Act Four: Q plays the part of game show host to the hilt as "Fact or Fiction" gets underway. Q-Too asks the first question, which is if the universe were about to end, how would you spend your final hours. Picard replies that he would read a good book, but no other sentient beings in the crowd "surveyed" agree. Beverly would like to be with her family, which scores 90 points. Riker says he would make love, bringing in another 460 points.

The opposing team is offered

the same questions. Chac'Maal says that he would spend his last few hours terminating Q, but no one agrees (which is kind of surprising considering Q's reputation). Aa'Tina would have sex, but she scores no points because that answer was already given. Baa'Lum would eat Beverly's liver, which actually gets them 270 points.

Taking camp humor into deep space nine, the bonus question is for them to name a particular tune: "the first strains of the theme music from the original *Star Trek* series." None of the Zaa-Narr can answer. Picard hits the buzzer. "My grandmother used to whistle this, the theme from 'Bonanza.'" A joyful Q responds, "Close enough. A classic from the same broadcast century. You win!" Picard's scoreboard shoots up to 960 points.

Q-Too is livid because that was *not* the right answer. She starts screaming at Chac'Maal, "Those broadcasts are playing your damn solar system right now!" The alien has no answer, but Q-Too no longer cares. She gets to choose the next game. Needless to say, yet another fight breaks out between the Qs. Picard attempts to intervene, telling them to shut up and then suggesting that they wrap things up with a duel to the death between he and Captain Chac'Maal. The only condition is that both crew are returned to normal. Chac'Maal steps forward, telling Picard that he accepts the challenge. Q-Too agrees.

They are on a planet in the midst of a sandstorm. In an arena à la Spartacus, the two Qs sit at a covered platform. Beneath them are two smaller platforms, the Zaa-Narrs on the left and Riker and Beverly on the right.

In the arena itself, Chac'Maal holds an alien trident and a long net, while Picard has a short sword and small shield. Picard draws first blood,

but Chac'Maal nets the captain. Picard uses his sword to stop the trident from skewering him. Chac'Maal attempts to stab him to death, but Picard moves out of the way. The fight continues, resulting in Chac'Maal getting Picard down on the ground and about to deliver the death blow. The alien hesitates to kill him. Q-Too delivers the "thumbs down" signal, but Chac'Maal refuses to kill him, stating, "Picard is a warrior, a man of honor. I have learned much from his human ways. He must live."

Q-Too is stunned, having never had a problem with the Zaa-Narr. Q is deleriously happy, because his team has won. Everyone appears back on the bridge of the Enterprise. Q-Too wants a rematch, but Picard refuses, pointing out that that wasn't part of the agreement. Q suggests that he and Q-Too go black hole bowling with comets. They argue again, giving Chac'Maal and his officers the chance to speak to Picard, expressing admiration. The captains salute each other as friends and the Zaa-Narr are transported back to their own ship. Q-Too is next to vanish. Q is thrilled, thanks Picard and vanishes as well.

Picard is ready to get back to the mission at hand, when Worf announces that all colonists from Xlapak Three are safely aboard the Enterprise.

"A parting gift from Q, no doubt," muses Riker.

"Well, at least we made new allies, Number One. Somewhere. Out there in space."

* * *

All in all, by perhaps losing a few of its campier moments, "I.Q. Test" would have been a fun Q adventure in the tradition of what's come before. Unfortunately, it never made it to the air.

"My basic mandate from Rick Berman when I came back fifth season, was to put more science fiction,

weirdness and humor in the show. He felt that the show had become too soap opery with too many small personal stories. I was given a choice of three or four stories they had. I did 'Power Play' and then there was this Q story, which had been bought by a first time writer and it was basically that there would be two Qs who were going to force our crew into an Olympics with other alien races. Rick Berman and Michael Piller said they wanted it funny, crazy and outrageous. I went away and came away a story, then I sat down with the entire staff and worked out the story over two days. They chose a game show and they chose a boxing match, they chose a shuttle race. I had to make those things interesting.

"One of the problems with writing these scripts is that the Qs talk a lot. One Q talks a lot, two Qs . . . So what happens to our regulars? Rick said, 'Don't worry about it, when Q comes on you just give him the show and write for the Qs. Then all these things seemed to expensive for a one hour episode, but I was told not to worry about it. So I wrote the script, feeling that it was different than the normal episode. I turned it in and the staff loved it, Rick Berman loved it and Michael Piller despised. He said it was not the kind of show he wanted to do and that was it."

Interestingly, there was a very strong possibility that Arnold Schwarzenegger would actually portray the alien captain.

"As I was writing the script, I said, 'Wait a minute, what if Arnold Schwarzenegger would do the show?' I happen to know a lot of people who know Arnold and I managed to work out the story in such a way that despite the fact he's our guest villain, he ends up becoming a good guy at the end. He actually wins and bends to Picard's humanity. He *would* have done it and I'm just sorry that it didn't work out."

THE STAR TREK FEATURES

Every feature film goes through various rewrites which result in key scenes being altered or dropped altogether. What follows is a look at William Shatner's original ending for *Star Trek V: The Final Frontier*, the aborted *Star Trek VI: Starfleet Academy* and the first take on *Star Trek: Generations*.

STAR TREK V THE LOST ENDING

A major complaint lodged against *Star Trek V* is that once the Enterprise broaches the final frontier in its search for God (after Spock's half-brother Sybok takes command of the vessel), everything else seems anti-climactic. Ironically, earlier drafts of the script had a much more extensive conclusion, which was cut due to budget over-runs.

Originally, the ending was far more exciting. Everything plays out exactly as it does in the film, with Kirk, Spock, McCoy and Sybok beaming down to the so-called God planet where all of them learn that whatever this being is, it *ain't* God.

"It would appear that the entity is trapped here," notes Spock. "This volcanic crater is the power source that contains him."

Kirk responds, "And if he gets his hands on the ship, he'll be able to spread himself across the galaxy."

"Precisely his intention!"

Sybok leaps into the crater, and both he and the demon disappear within it as fire fills the sky. Kirk, Spock and McCoy make a run for it after hearing a horrible shrieking sound, that turns out to be numerous living gargoyles spewing from the crater. Running for their lives, the group is slowed down by McCoy, who falls off a ledge and breaks his leg. Kirk carries the doctor as they make their way to the shuttle.

Once inside the shuttle, they are unable to take off as the gargoyles have arrived, and torn apart the thruster units. Kirk contacts Scotty and is told that he can beam them up one at a time. Bones is first to go, then Spock.

Cut to the Enterprise, Scotty activates the transporter beam for Kirk, and actually beams aboard a gargoyle who has grabbed the captain's communicator. Freaking out, Scotty picks up a hand phaser and destroys the creature, but in so doing he also accidentally destroys the transporter. *There's no way to bring Kirk back up!!*

As the Klingon Bird of Prey approaches, Spock is struck by an idea and goes to Klingon General Korrd, now on board Enterprise. The man is resistant to help, but Spock responds, "Damn you, sir, you will try!"

Back on the planet, Kirk is being pursued by the gargoyles. He free-climbs a small mountain (much as he did at the film's beginning) and reaches the top. Armed with two hand phasers, he kills as many of the creatures as he can, but their numbers are legion. It looks like curtains for James T. Kirk. But then, the Bird of Prey decloaks, the machine gun phaser weapon lowers into frame and starts firing, blowing the gargoyles apart, and sending the rest scurrying back to the pit from which they came. Kirk stares at the ship.

"You want me, you Klingon bastards? Come and get me!" he screams, firing the hand phasers at the vessel. As in the film, he is brought to the bridge, where he finds that Spock is the gunner. Much of the remainder of the script plays out as it did in the final version, although more mention is made of the fact that the rescuing of Klingon, Romulan and human hostages will result in a better understanding between their races, and a path toward the future – actually toward *The Next Generation*.

Spock notes that Sybok has turned out to be a false prophet, but Kirk isn't sure.

"He may have been misguided," notes the captain, "but perhaps his cause has served a higher purpose. The Federation, the Romulans, the Klingons – none of us – will ever be able to see each other again in quite the same light. We have Sybok to thank for that."

Certainly a more exciting finale to such an intense build-up.

Explains screenwriter David Loughery, "When the torpedo came down and explodes the hole, it's like the bottle is uncapped and all the imps spill out, free, and chase our characters back to the shuttle. That was our original concept. A movie, especially a movie like this one, goes through so many transformations from original story to final film. Because of all the hands involved in the making of these movies, it sometimes starts to take on a committee atmosphere to moviemaking. Things don't turn out *exactly* the way you originally wanted them to, but there are reasons for that.

"We certainly wish we could have hung on to some of that concept. The area of the movie that has always been in flux is *how* we represent the God-being. That sequence got lost when it became financially impossible for us to create the gargoyle creatures. That was really more of a budgetary concession than anything else. You're always sorry to see those things go, because your imagination is one thing and the budget is something else. In various places, we had to make certain cuts and rearrangements based on how much we could afford. In the best of all worlds, you usually throw everything in the first draft and it gets pared down. Frankly, there is a point where Paramount will *not* finance these movies. They have a line that they draw, and that's just the way it is. Everyone else says, 'Oh, for crying out loud, it's going to make money,' but they have their line.

"As a writer," he elaborates, "you're always saying, 'I wish they had stuck to the earlier draft, it was better during draft three,' or something like that. You always have your rationalization, and a dream-picture in your mind of what it *should* look like. But, a picture takes on its own reality once it starts being shot. After a certain period, you really don't have very much influence over how they turn out. You have to take the good with the bad. I don't feel badly about it, but I just wish some things had been better, because it would have given us more of a chance."

STAR TREK VI STARFLEET ACADEMY

After the chilly box-office reception of *Star Trek V* and the continuing chorus of naysayers criticizing the cast as being too old to continue, many suspected the silver screen voyages of the starship Enterprise had truly passed into the final frontier. But Producer Harve Bennett, in conjunction with *Star Trek V* screenwriter David Loughery, was hard at work creating a new vehicle to continue the *Star Trek* movie missions.

"Every time they go to make one of these *Star Trek* movies," notes Loughery, "the producers and the studio always run into the same problem in getting the original cast together. The reasons for that are money, power, creative differences, ego, health, unavailability . . . all of those things. Harve always had this ace up his sleeve, which was if we can't get everybody together for one of these *Star Trek* movies, we should do a prequel."

Called *Starfleet Academy*, the proposed film would have chronicled a young Kirk, Spock and McCoy's days at the Academy, as part of *Trek*'s 25th anniversary celebration. Instead, a sixth and final film featuring the original "classic" cast was put into production by Paramount, resulting in Harve Bennett's departure from the series.

"We had a better movie and we had a film that would have allowed them to make the same *Star Trek VI* eighteen months later," says Bennett of *Starfleet Academy*, which was aborted after objections from fans made the project untenable.

"I think there was a fat chance of that happening," comments Walter Koenig. "I can't read Harve's mind, but if *Starfleet Academy* had done well, they would have gone on with that group. If it hadn't, they probably would have abandoned the whole project."

"Because of the way *Star Trek VI* was sold – don't miss your chance to say good-bye – it's unlikely that *Starfleet Academy*, which asks 'Would you like to know how it all happened?' will be made," continues Bennett, whose previous producing chores included work on *The Mod Squad, The Six Million Dollar Man,* the Emmy Award winning miniseries *A Woman Called Golda* and *The Jesse Owens Story.*

Starfleet Academy chronicled the story of a young James T. Kirk, a Spock who is estranged from his parents and becomes the first Vulcan to attend Starfleet Academy, and Leonard McCoy, a 30 year old doctor who attends the Academy after having pulled the plug on his terminally ill father and is searching for meaning in his life. Michael Curtiz's 1940 film, *The Santa Fe Trail,* served as an inspiration for what Bennett envisioned as the classic triumvirate's first trek. The film which could have been made, according to Bennett, for $27 million would also have avoided the hefty multi-million dollar salaries of its leads – Shatner and Nimoy – as well as Kelley's take-home of nearly a half a million dollars and the $125,000 paychecks the supporting players pocketed.

"I pitched the idea to Harve at his daughter's Bar Mitzvah," recalls *Trek VI* producer Ralph Winter. "We had already locked in the *Star Trek IV* storyline with the whales and I said, 'You know, I have a great idea, let's do a prequel' in the middle of this reception for his daughter. I suggested we develop a series of films to be another franchise, another tent pole that we could open. We could do a prequel and find out how Kirk and Spock met at the Starfleet Academy. When we were doing *Star Trek V,* we got the studio to approve work on the script. It is an excellent story, but it has been misperceived. It's a great story finding out about this young cocky character on a farm who goes to flight school and meets up with

the first alien that comes from Vulcan and how they meet the other characters. It would have been a gift for the fans on the 25th anniversary."

David Loughery notes, "When I heard about the idea, I thought it was terrific. Not from the point of view of recasting, but from the point of view of storytelling, because I worked so closely with these characters on *Star Trek V,* that the idea of doing an origin story – where you show them as young cadets and kids – was tremendously exciting. What it was, was a real coming of age story. In outline form, it was the story of Kirk and Spock meeting for the first time as cadets here on Earth. We've got a young Jim Kirk, who's kind of cocky and wild. He's not exactly what you might think starship captain material might be. He's like one of these kids who would rather fly hot planes and chase girls. Spock is this brilliant, arrogant, aloof to the point of obnoxiousness, genius. It's this mask he's hiding behind to cover his own conflicting human emotions. He's an outcast, he left Vulcan in shame against his father's wishes and, like all adolescents, he's trying to find a place to fit in, but he keeps screwing it up.

"Over the course of this story," he continues, "which is one year at Starfleet Academy, Kirk and Spock are sort of put to the test and they begin as rivals and end up as friends and comrades who learn that they have to combine their talents for the first time to defeat a deadly enemy. In the final scene, where they say good-bye at graduation and go their separate ways, we're able to see the legends that these two boys are going to grow up to become."

But for Bennett, who had spent a decade living with *Star Trek, Starfleet Academy* was not to be. The rejection of the project was a big disappointment for the veteran producer who planned the film as his freshman directorial effort.

"It meant a lot to me because I

came out of UCLA film school wanting to be a director and other winds blew me to to other ports," says Bennett. "It was a desire of mine to direct and it was accepted by the studio and, the fact is, part of the deal was for us to do a *Star Trek VI*, with the original cast after *Starfleet Academy*."

But once word leaked out about the project, support was marshalled against the film and vociferously denounced on the convention circuit by members of the supporting cast, as well as *Star Trek* creator Gene Roddenberry.

Said Roddenberry in the pages of *Cinefantastique*, "I didn't like it. Who was going to cast the new Kirk and Spock? No one has ever cast a *Trek* character besides me that's worked. Braggadocio or whatever, that is the history of *Trek*. It wasn't good. Some of it was like *Police Academy*. You could hardly do this without the magic of a group of characters tailored for *Star Trek*, which this was not."

Letters began to pour into Paramount decrying the planned feature as heresy.

"We were really caught off guard and surprised by the fans who reacted so negatively to the idea of this movie," admits David Loughery. "Somehow they conceived it as sort of a spoof or a takeoff. That's where we got off on the wrong foot. The fans had misinformation, which may have been put out there by people for their own reasons. Certainly if we were going to make a movie like that, it meant that Walter and whoever wouldn't get that job a year or two down the line that they had come to expect. I don't know if that's the case, but I do know that the misinformation released had people convinced that we were going to do a cross between *Police Academy* and *The Jetsons*. It was never that kind of story. I think it's traditional that the fans have objected to different things. Harve's always been smart enough to double-cross them; give

them what they've objected to, but surprise them with something that makes it good and worthwhile. We felt that there was a powerful story there, one that the audience would be interested in. We're always interested in young Indiana Jones and young Sherlock Holmes, and how they started and came to be who they are. This was sort of the way to explain Kirk and Spock and where they came from."

"There *was* pressure from a lot of people not to do this," Bennett emphasizes. "I don't think there was any question that the self-interest of the supporting cast was not served by it and if I was George Takei, I would do exactly what he did and if I were Jimmy Doohan, I would be a really unhappy man. The only one I'm really furious at though is Jimmy Doohan. He said I was fired and I can't abide lies. My term was up and I was offered $1.5 million to do *Star Trek VI* and I said, 'Thanks, I don't wish to do that. I want to do the Academy.'"

Responds Doohan, "I was impressed with Harve when he first came in and did *Star Trek II* and *III*, but I think he got a little greedy. He wanted things his own way. He wanted to take over *Star Trek* for himself. What the heck, you don't do that sort of thing, trying to destroy instead of building. He obviously did not realize the strength of the old cast. The whole thing would have been starting out as if from scratch. I think it was [Frank] Mancuso who didn't realize we were not going to be in it. When he found out, [he] said goodbye Harve."

"My last words to Mancuso before he was asked to leave [by the then recently installed head of Paramount, Stanley Jaffe] was if it was a question of anyone's concerns about my directing, I'd back off on that," says Bennett. "They then offered me *Star Trek VI* and gave me a pay or play commitment to direct and produce *Starfleet Academy* afterwards. My position was, and I think it was cor-

rect, that they would pay me to do *VI* and make the movie which would have been a real big, fat check for me and never made *Starfleet Academy*. To be paid off because the movie I might have done, which is being done by others, would close the franchise was not my intention. I had a life, it's not like I hadn't done anything else before *Star Trek*. The *Star Trek* curse is something that the poor supporting cast has to live with, but I don't."

Opines William Shatner, "Harve was striving to find an answer for the studio's question 'Are these guys too old to continue?' So he tried to find a solution as a storywriter and he must of said here's a way of going. Apparently everybody agreed, but at some point they shut him down after preparing this production for a year and he got very upset about it and left. I wasn't too clued in on the politics of what was happening. I had heard about the prequel and was considering my options, but it was never approved and we didn't know whether or not there would be another *Star Trek* until the last second."

Bennett holds the supporting cast entirely accountable for the film's demise. "Their jobs and livelihoods were jeopardized," he says. "You have to understand there's good news and bad news for these people. They are the principal bearers of the *Star Trek* curse. The good news is everybody loves them and the bad news is they can't work anywhere else. They have managed to generate handsome incomes, some more than others, by tapping the convention and lecture circuit. That's fine, they're entitled to do that because no one is casting Uhura and George Takei because they're so identifiable and they become liabilities in other material. *Starfleet Academy*, like *Star Trek IV*, would have reached beyond the cult. It would have interested people who had never seen a *Star Trek* film which did not include the regulars, but it simply said, if you don't understand what it's all about, come see how it all began."

For Ralph Winter, *Starfleet Academy* would have ushered in a new approach to the *Star Trek* franchise for the studio in which a coherent plan would be created for producing the *Trek* films on a semi-regular basis as opposed to the sporadic, fitful stop and go start-up on a new film every three years with the arduous contract negotiations that initiating each new chapter entailed.

"*Starfleet Academy* may have looked like a mistake," says Winter, "but look at the franchise as a whole. We have a successful series of feature films, then a new television series and with the film series ending it made sense to start a new series of films. You could have opened a whole new frontier. When *Star Trek: The Next Generation* came out, the people said this will never work, how can we have a new Captain? It will never equal Kirk and Spock. But they've achieved their own success. It could have been the same with a prequel cast, now you would have three different fronts. Make the successful features with the original cast, features with a prequel cast and the television series with the new cast. That's what could have happened. You look at the long term and you develop two or three scripts at a time and you maximize production. The unfortunate part about today's economy and the thinking of these big companies is let's see how this one does and then we'll decide on the next one. There was never a plan after any of these films to do another one. *Star Trek II* was the last picture, Spock was dead. That was it. It's just getting too expensive to drag out all the wardrobe, sets, models. With a long term plan you could milk this forever and the fans would be thrilled, but if you go one step at a time and don't know where you're going, then the films are expensive and maybe it does make sense to do the sixth film with the original cast."

As for the *Star Trek VI* that did materialize on the screen, Bennett has mixed feelings. "I'm sure glad that it's not my movie," he muses. "I was presented with the choice of doing *Star Trek VI* in 11 months and I didn't want to do a conventional film and I didn't believe I could do it in that time. The fact that they did it is a tribute to all my buddies, and they are good buddies. Nicholas Meyer is the fastest writer in the world, Ralph Winter is the most ethical and perfect producer of special effects movies anywhere and one of the nicest men I've ever know. It wasn't easy to walk away from that, but if your heart is not in something and you've earned the right not to have do things that cause you pain, then you don't do them."

In terms of the future of *Starfleet Academy*, as the saying goes in the *Star Trek* universe: "There are always possibilities."

STAR TREK: GENERATIONS TAKE ONE

When Paramount Pictures initially decided to transport the crew of *Star Trek: The Next Generation* from syndication to feature films, executive producer Rick Berman put two screenplays into work. One of them, the basis of *Star Trek: Generations*, was written by Ron Moore and Brannon Braga. The other, unfilmed script, was penned by Maurice Hurley.

Hurley, who had served as a co-executive producer of the series in its early days, and whose greatest contribution was probably the introduction of the cybernetic race, the Borg, describes his screenplay as "a great adventure."

Although ultimately not chosen, it promised quite a ride for fans of the defunct series.

"There was basically a fold in space," Hurley explains, "and an adversary who had been in a battle was blown through it into our universe. It is trying to get home to save its species, but in order to do that — and in order to get home — it has to basically destroy us."

The analogy he draws is to a parent in a schoolyard with his two-year-old child, with the parent on one end and the child on the other. The child is in a dangerous situation, about to die.

"You rush across the schoolyard," he proposes, "stepping on toes, knocking down children, breaking bones, and smashing heads to get to your baby. Then you save your baby and you look back at all the mayhem and chaos and blood that you have caused among all these other two-year-old children. You could have killed one of them, but it wouldn't have made a difference to you until after the fact when you looked back and said, 'Oh my God,

what did I do? I'm sorry, but I just didn't have a choice.' That's the story. These other people who are here and are about to destroy us are basically saying, 'Sorry, but there's nothing we can do about it. You're all going to have to die.'"

Although the Enterprise is sent out to dispatch this adversary, Picard senses that all is not as it seems with the alien; that the destruction being caused must have a purpose, though it seemingly doesn't.

"Picard senses that there's something else going on here because he finds no subtext for the attack, and all battles have subtext," Hurley points out. "In a battle with a Klingon or Romulan there's a subtext and you can define what that subtext is. Romulans want to kick your ass and in the process of kicking your ass they want you to know how damn smart and superior they are. These people have no subtext and Picard says that's wrong. They have to have one. What is it? That among other things starts him investigating, causing him to veer one way where, on the surface, it seems he should be veering the other way."

Part of Picard's investigation is to go to the holodeck to call up the image of Captain James T. Kirk (the only classic character used in the screenplay), who experienced a similar situation in the original series episode, "The Tholian Web," in which the captain, on board the U.S.S. Defiant, is trapped in another dimension.

"It's the only other time on record that it ever happened," Hurley notes, "and the only other person who ever witnessed it was Kirk. So Picard and Kirk have witnessed, separated by time, similar events. Now you want to say, 'Wait a minute, I see it this way, how do you see it? Did it happen to you the same way it happened to me? If it was different, how was it different?' It was Picard's attempt to get an emotional point of view, or another point of view, from

the Kirk character that differed from what he was getting from pure facts. For instance, if you describe an event for me and I read it and you say, 'The sky was red and there was a lot of noise,' well, what does that mean to me? What is red? What red are you talking about? What kind of noise? Relate it to something for me.

"If you're dead and all I have is your writings, I have no way of knowing that. If I can go back and talk to you, when you say red you absolutely see a color. So do I. Your color red might be fire engine and mine might be maroon. If I know that, that alters how I view what you're saying. Noise also means something. What's noise to me, what's noise to you? You know what those answers are. The computer would just put down noise, but if the computer regenerated you in terms of a sense of who you are, how you viewed noise is presumably how you would still view it. So I get the subtlety from the personal interview that I don't get off the page.

"But that's not enough," he continues, "so he starts manipulating the image so it basically becomes a couple of bizarre scenes between Picard and Kirk and it gets confrontational at certain moments. You want to bring back Kirk and not have it get confrontational? Kirk will get confrontational with anyone. In *Star Trek V*, he got confrontational with God! So it became a way to put those two classic characters and two really great actors together, and let them bang on each other."

Despite the fact that Berman has indicated Hurley's script could be filmed as a sequel to the current film, the writer doesn't think it's likely to happen.

"Everything has it's time," says Hurley philosophically, "and it's seldom that somebody goes back to the pot. It's a good idea and a good story that Rick Berman and I worked hard on. But that's just the way it is."